13.95

T0032354

WITHDRAWN

004606

LICHENS

An Illustrated Guide

by

Frank Dobson

PERSHORE COLLEGE OF HORTICULTURE
LIBRARY

2/89

CLASS WITHDRAWN NUMBER

582.29

8628

Rp

THE RICHMOND PUBLISHING CO. LTD.

To Dennis W. Bloodworth whose skill as a teacher first awoke my interest in botany.

First edition 1979
Second revised and corrected edition 1981

© F. S. Dobson 1979 and 1981

All rights reserved.
No part of the publication may be reproduced in any form or by any means, electronically, mechanically, by photocopying, recording or otherwise, without the prior permission of the copyright owners.

ISBN 0 85546 210 8 CASED
ISBN 0 85546 133 0 PAPER
Published By The Richmond Publishing Co. Ltd.
Orchard Road, Richmond, Surrey, England.

Printed in Great Britain by
Kingprint Limited, Richmond, Surrey

CONTENTS

Cover illustration: *Parmelia caperata*

ACKNOWLEDGMENTS

It would be difficult to write a book such as this without the assistance of many people and Institutes. In particular I would like to mention, Mr P.W. James, Dr F. Rose, Mr J.R. Laundon and the Department of Botany, British Museum (Natural History). I am also indebted to The British Lichen Society for permission to use data collected for their mapping scheme and to Dr C.J.B Hitch for his assistance in seeing that I obtained the relevant information. Members of the British Lichen Society and students on courses run by the Field Studies Council have all been very helpful with suggestions and in testing out the keys. Dr U.K. Duncan must be thanked for revitalising British lichenology and the debt owed to her shows in the pages of this book. Special thanks must be given to Dr D.L. Hawksworth for the invaluable assistance that he has given me. I am extremely grateful for all this assistance, and without it, it would have been almost impossible to produce this book. However I must stress that any errors contained in this book are mine alone, as is the rather personal choice of rarer species included.

Second Edition

I must also thank Mr. R. Miller for his sterling work in correcting the typographical errors in the first edition. I am also grateful to Dr. D. L. Hawksworth for the checklist of recent changes in nomenclature.

INTRODUCTION

Lichens are stable, consistent and identifiable combinations between an alga and a fungus. It is however difficult to define them more closely than this, indeed a number of species are studied by 'lichenologists' even though there is evidence that the fungal partner exists on its own without the aid of an alga. On the other hand some stable relationships between fungi and algae are traditionally ignored by 'lichenologists'.

The shape of the thallus is usually dictated by the fungal partner but even this is not consistent, as in some cases, where two or more algae are present in one lichen (usually a blue-green alga and a green alga), these may produce very different forms in the same thallus. In the case of the filamentous lichens these clearly follow the thread-like form of the alga.

There are a few basidiomycete, hyphomycete and phycomycete genera of lichens but the vast majority are ascomycetes, producing their spores in sac-like asci. In Britain there are about 10 lichenized basidiomycetes; all the other species are ascomycetes. It has been said that most lichens are ascomycetes with an unusual mode of nutrition, but out of over 30,000 species forming the Ascomycotina, over half of them are lichenized; therefore lichenization is the most common life-style of the ascomycetes.

This problem has produced difficulties of definition for many centuries and lichens were at one time classified with the mosses. In common with other fungi, the fungal partner is unable to photosynthesise and produce its own food in order to survive, other fungi overcome this problem by breaking down living or dead organic material. In the case of lichens this food is obtained from the excess sugars that the fungus appears to stimulate the algal partner to produce. For many years the algal cells were not recognised as such by botanists and were often thought to be the reproductive cells of the lichen. When Schwendener in the mid-nineteenth century suggested the true nature of a lichen he was reviled and his views of a fungal/algal relationship were not generally accepted for a considerable period.

The advantages to the fungus are fairly clear; it obtains from its partner the sugars needed to provide the energy for survival, growth and reproduction. The advantages to the alga are, however, very doubtful. It has been suggested that it has protection from the extremes of temperature, light and moisture and possibly obtains mineral salts leached by the fungus from the substrate. Recent research has shown that these proposed advantages are of dubious significance and that it may be that the fungus is more or less a parasite on the alga and the shape assumed by a lichen species is such that the algal cells are displayed to maximum advantage of the fungus for that particular ecological niche. Whatever the final outcome of this research, it is clear that the relationship is very successful and lichens have been able to colonize many habitats from below sea level to the tops of mountains, and from the cold polar regions to the baking heat of deserts, outnumbering the flowering plants in many harsh environments. Some species grow less than a millimetre a year but against this,some are able to survive for possibly thousands of years.

When there is a combination of different organisms, such as in lichens, there is often a problem of dispersal and propagation. Very many lichens produce fruiting bodies and the shape and structure of these, and the spores they contain, forms the basis of most lichen classification. The major problem for the propagation of the lichen is that these fruiting bodies are only produced by the fungal partner. Although unlike many other fungi these fruiting bodies are long-lived and can often produce spores for several years, they do not contain any reproductive element from the alga.

Most of the algae found in lichens can also be found free-growing, but the fungal partner is never found free-growing and if it is grown on its own in a laboratory, it usually forms a rather shapeless mass that in no way resembles the form of the complete lichen. This means that after dispersal, when the spore germinates, it must quickly obtain suitable algal cells to incorporate into the potential lichen or it will die. There is now sufficient evidence to suggest that in some cases it does this by parasitising another lichen containing a suitable alga and taking this alga over for its own use. Despite the considerable number of spores produced, the chances are still against frequent successful reproduction by this means. In many species the importance of vegetative means of dispersal is high, indeed some species have never been found with fruiting bodies. These vegetative propagules consist of a number of algal cells and fungal hyphae that may simply be broken fragments of thallus or they may be formed in special structures (soralia and isidia). These propagules are then carried away by many means, such as wind, rain, insects or on animals. If they arrive on a suitable substrate it may then be possible for them to grow and develop into another complete lichen.

There are about 1400 species of lichen in Britain but many of these are very rare and the almost 500 species included in this book cover nearly all those that are likely to be readily found. The study of lichens has the advantage over the study of most other British plants in that they have the same form throughout the year and they may be collected in the winter or summer alike. Care should however be taken not to collect very rare species and even the common ones should only be collected if it still leaves a viable number of specimens at any particular site. Permission from the landowner should be obtained before collecting in any area, and the "Country-code" must be followed, in some circumstances it is now an offence to collect without the owner's permission.

Collecting requires only simple equipment and as long as the specimens collected are dried fairly quickly (such as over a warm radiator) they should not go mouldy and as long as they are kept dry, are usually little subjected to the attacks of insects and mould. The following equipment should be obtained by anyone seriously indulging in lichenology.

A stout knife for removing specimens from trees, wood, etc., (not folding, as these can cause an accident if they close up when in use).

A hammer (preferably a geological hammer or at least a hammer with a flat, secure head).

A selection of sharp, cold chisels and a pair of protective glasses or goggles.

Sheets of paper or packets in which to place the specimens after collection (damp specimens in polythene bags go mouldy very quickly).

As specimens are collected they should be individually wrapped as they can very easily become useless by rubbing against each other. Details of where and when the specimen was collected should be written on the packet as soon as the specimen is placed inside.

When the specimen has been identified, and if it is going to be filed away, the following is the minimum information that will be required if the specimen is to have any scientific use:

Name of species.

Place collected (if possible including the grid references or at least the name of the Vice-county).

Date collected.

Substrate.

Name of collector and, if different, the name of the person who identified the specimen.

Do not forget when identifying a specimen that the colour often changes when it is wet, in some species from a silvery grey to almost black. It will soon be found that the spores form such an important part of classification that access to a microscope in order to examine these minute bodies is essential to any serious lichenologist. In order to examine the spores a "squash" must be made. This is done by removing a small piece of the fruiting body (within reason the smaller the better) and placing it on a microscope slide, a drop of water is added and left for two or three minutes. Alternatively the specimen may be moistened before it is sliced. A cover slip is then placed on top and if the end of a pencil is dropped lightly down onto it from about 1" this will usually squash the specimen sufficently for examination . If required the specimen will soften more easily and rapidly in the K solution (but keep the solution off the microscope lens) and/or more pressure can be applied to spread the specimen on the slide.

Many lichens contain very stable substances (specimen in collections a hundred or more years old can be tested) that react to give colour changes with several simple chemicals. These changes are very valuable in identification but it must be remembered that although a positive test can be considered conclusive a negative one may only mean that the specimen has a low percentage of the substance for which the test is made. In this case test another part of the thallus. If it is the cortex that is to be tested (in this book this is the case unless otherwise given) a drop of the chemical is placed on the upper surface of the thallus. The chemicals are only used in very small quantities and are best applied with a glass rod or a cocktail stick. These chemicals however often change the colour of the lichen by making the cortex translucent, if there is any doubt about a colour change, take up the liquid on a small piece of white absorbent paper and examine this. In a number of cases it is the medulla and not the cortex that is examined. To expose the medulla cut away the upper cortex of the lichen at a low angle when the medulla (white in most species) will be exposed.

The following are the most common of the simple thalline chemical tests.

K = potassium hydroxide. About a 10% solution is required but the concentration is not too critical. This forms a stable solution that will keep for many months in a closed bottle. Many of the yellow reactions are best seen by taking up the drop of chemical from the thallus under test on white absorbent paper.

C = calcium hypochlorite. This is the main constituent of many household bleaching liquids. It is only active for a few months but fortunately the low cost enables it to be replaced at frequent intervals. It should however also be tested at frequent intervals (eg. *Ochrolechia androgyna* or *O. tartarea* turn red). The reaction is often fleeting and may only last a few seconds, so the test should performed while the specimen is being examined under a lens.

K C. K is applied to the specimen and after about 30 seconds is taken up with absorbent paper. A drop of C is then placed onto the paper next to the K. Where they intermingle the colour change should occur (often fugative).

C K This is the reverse of the previous test with the C being applied followed by the K. This test is important in identifying diffractaic acid and is rarely used.

P or Pd = Paraphenylenediamine This is unstable and is used by wetting a crystal with alcohol and applying the liquid to the specimen. A fairly stable solution may be made as Steiner's Solution (1gm paraphenylenediamine, 10gm sodium sulphite, two or three drops of wetting agent (domestic liquid detergent), 100 ml water). This solution should last for up to 3 months but should be tested at intervals (the medulla of *Parmelia sulcata* turns yellow to red). The reaction with P often takes two or three minutes to develop and a specimen should be tested several times before a negative result is declared. As they are poisonous all these chemicals should be handled with great care, but P is thought to be carcinogenic and extra care should be taken in using it. If even a minute crystal falls on paper it will, over a period, produce a strong brown stain.

I = Iodine is used in a few tests where the presence or absence of isolichenin (a starch like product) is important. Meltzer's reagent can be used for this purpose (0.5 gm iodine in 1 gm potassium iodide plus 20 ml chloral hydrate and 25 ml water). Test on the spores of *Graphis* which turn blue-purple.

Meltzer's reagent is also useful in squash preparations where it is important to see the septa of spores more clearly.

The substances being tested for are often most concentrated just behind the growing point, but take care to watch closely in those cases where the reaction fades very quickly.

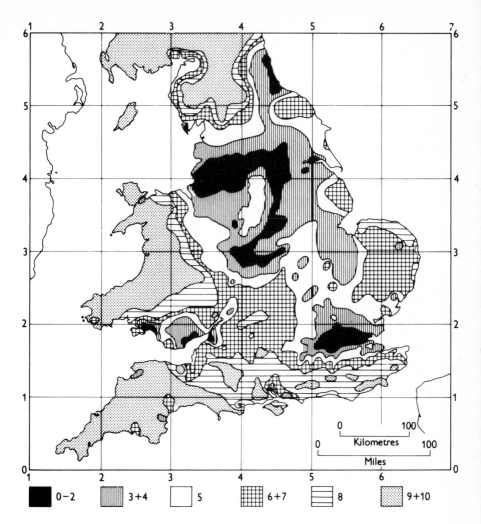

| ■ 0-2 | ▦ 3+4 | ☐ 5 | ▦ 6+7 | ▤ 8 | ▥ 9+10 |

APPROXIMATE POSITIONS OF AIR POLLUTION ZONES.
There are however many small areas of variation which cannot
be shown on a map of this scale. In most cases these are areas
of higher air pollution and will come into a lower zone than
shown on the above map. In some cases the zone may be higher
than shown above; such a case would be a narrow valley where
most of the pollution is blown over the top by the prevailing
wind. The level of pollution may also vary for other reasons; for
example the centre of a wood may have lower pollution near the
ground than in a similar position near to the edges of the wood.
All these factors must be considered when deciding from the
above map, the zone in which any particular site is situated.

Zone

0 Epiphytes absent

1 *Pleurococcus viridis* s.l. present but confined to the base

2 *Pleurococcus viridis* extends up the trunk; *Lecanora conizaeoides* present but confined to the bases

3 *Lecanora conizaeoides* extends up the trunk; *Lepraria incana* becomes frequent on the bases

4 *Hypogymnia physodes* and/or *Parmelia saxatilis,* or *P. sulcata* appear on the bases, do not extend up the trunks. *Lecidea scalaris, Lecanora expallens* and *Chaenotheca ferruginea* often present

5 *Hypogymnia physodes* or *P. saxatilis* extends up the trunk to 2.5m or more; *P. glabratula, P. subrudecta, Parmeliopsis ambigua* and *Lecanora chlarotera* appear; *Calicium viride, Lepraria candelaris* and *Pertusaria amara* may occur; *Ramalina farinacea* and *Evernia prunastri* if present largely confined to the bases; *Platismatia glauca* may be present on horizontal branches

6 *P. caperata* present at least on the base; rich in species of *Pertusaria* (e.g., *P. albescens, P. hymenea)* and *Parmelia* (e.g., *P. revoluta* (except in NE), *P. tiliacea, P. exasperatula* (in N)); *Graphis elegans* appearing; *Pseudevernia furfuracea* and *Alectoria fuscescens* present in upland areas

7 *Parmelia caperata, P. revoluta* (except in NE), *P. tiliacea, P. exasperatula* (in N) extend up the trunk; *Usnea subfloridana, Pertusaria hemisphaerica, Rinodina roboris* (in S) and *Arthonia impolita* (in E) appear

8 *Usnea ceratina, Parmelia perlata* or *P. reticulata* (S and W) appear; *Rinodina roboris* extends up the trunk (in S); *Normandina pulchella* and *U. rubiginea* (in S) usually present

9 *Lobaria pulmonaria, L. amplissima, Pachyphiale cornea, Dimerella lutea,* or *Usnea florida* present; if these absent crustose flora well developed with often more than 25 species on larger well-lit trees

10 *L. amplissima, L. scrobiculata, Sticta limbata, Pannaria* spp., *Usnea articulata, U. filipendula* or *Teloschistes flavicans* present to locally abundant

Basic or nutrient-enriched bark	*Mean winter SO_2 (ug/m^3)*
Epiphytes absent	?
Pleurococcus viridis s.l. extends up the trunk	> 170
Lecanora conizaeoides abundant; *L. expallens* occurs occasionally on the bases	About 150
Lecanora expallens and *Buellia punctata* abundant *B. canescens* appears	About 125
Buellia canescens common; *Physcia adscendens* and *Xanthoria parietina* appear on the bases; *Physcia tribacia* appear in S	About 70
Physconia grisea, P. farrea, Buellia alboatra, Physcia orbicularis, P. tenella, Ramalina farinacea, Haematomma ochroleucum var. *porphyrium, Schismatomma decolorans, Xanthoria candelaria, Opegrapha varia* and *O. vulgata* appear; *Buellia canescens* and *X. parietina* common; *Parmelia acetabulum* appear in E	About 60
Pertusaria albescens, Physconia pulverulenta, Physciopsis adglutinata, arthopyrenia gemmata, Caloplaca luteoalba, Xanthoria polycarpa and *Lecania cyrtella* appear; *Physcia orbicularis, Opegrapha varia* and *O. vulgata* become abundant	About 50
Physcia aipolia, Anaptychia ciliaris, Bacidia rubella, Ramalina fastigiata, Candelaria concolor and *Arthopyrenia biformis* appear	About 40
Physcia aipolia abundant; *Anaptychia ciliaris* occurs in fruit; *Parmelia perlata, P. reticulata* (in S and W), *Gyalecta flotowii, Ramalina baltica, R. pollinaria* and *Desmazieria evernioides* appear	About 35
Ramalina calicaris, R. fraxinea, R. subfarinacea, Physcia leptalea, Caloplaca aurantiaca and *C. cerina* appear	Under 30
As 9	'Pure'

LAYOUT OF THE ENTRIES

The main body of the book is laid out in alphabetic order according to genus. Where there have been recent changes in genera which could not be adjusted in the layout, the locations of these genera can be found in the index.

Each genus commences with its main characteristics (and in some cases those of the family) together with illustrations of spores, paraphyses, etc. Many of these illustrations have been drawn directly from slides, but in other cases, the details have been derived from many sources and therefore these illustrations should be used for general guidance only. The information in this section is not usually repeated under each species and it should always be consulted in identifying a specimen. Either a table of characteristics or a key to the species then follows. These keys are designed for use only with the entries in this book. It is possible that using them, or the data under the species entries, they may also agree with a rare species not included in this book. To aid recognition the species entries are frequently subdivided into groups relating to habitat or prominent characters. The species entries give a description, any simple chemical reactions of importance (unless otherwise mentioned they refer to the reactions of the cortex) and in most instances a photograph is then provided. As far as possible these have been chosen to show the more important features and are usually of average specimens such as are likely to be found rather than rare but superb ones.

In the reactions given in this book the colour changes are abbreviated as follows y = yellow, o = orange, r = red, c = crimson, p = purple, o–r = orange to red, b = blue, f = faint.

A new check-list by Hawksworth, Coppins and James was being prepared when this book went to press but as that list was not complete, there are a number of discrepencies between it and the names used in this book. Where it was not possible to change the position of an entry the more recent name is shown in square brackets [ ]. Where a species is still frequently referred to by an older synonym this is shown in curved brackets ( ).

THE MAPS

The maps are based on the best evidence available but a great deal has still to be learnt regarding the distribution of British lichens, and this is an aspect of lichenology where the amateur can be of much assistance. This is especially the case with Ireland where the small number of records or completely blank maps, in many cases reflect the lack of data rather than the absence of a species. Many of the maps are based on data collected for the British Lichen Society mapping scheme and these maps have the symbol 'O' in the bottom left hand corner. These maps show where a species has been recorded, but again the lack of a black dot may only be due to an area being under recorded; however most of the maps show a clear pattern of distribution. The other maps are drawn from the opinions of a number of British lichenologists as to the distribution of a species. It must be remembered that although a black area is shown on a map many factors such as a lack of a suitable substrate or too high a pollution level will lead to the absence of a species. The appropriate level of air pollution that can be tolerated by a species is given in the scale (1 to 10) in the top left hand corner of the map (see pages xi to xiii for an explanation of this scale). In some cases such as where a species grows in the sea or there is considerable doubt over the pollution tolerance this code is not given.

The letter "C" under a map denotes an illustration in the colour section. These have been selected to differ in most cases from those in "Common British Lichens" (Dobson 1979) and it is thus possible to obtain cheaply about 40 further colour illustrations to supplement those given here.

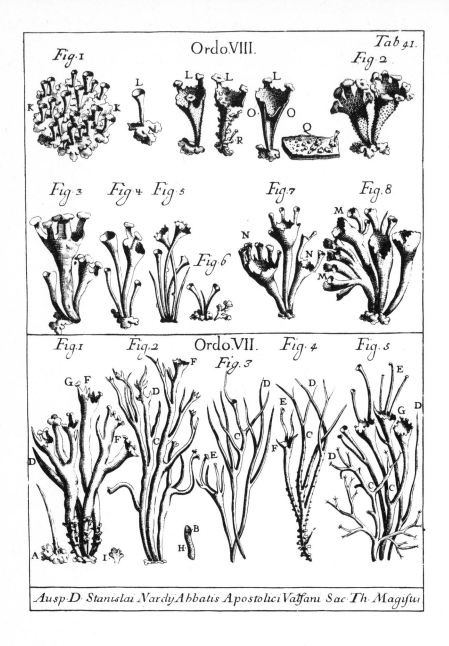

An example of an early lichen illustration, which, together with the engravings at the end of some sections in this book, was taken from *Nova Plantarum Genera* by P.A. Micheli. This was first published in Florence in 1729.

This key is designed for use for only those species that are included in this book. It may not 'key-out' correctly for other species. If a rare species is found that is not included in this book, the genus can, in many cases, be deduced from the group key and then from the main key by using the spore details.

A number of species will be found to spread from their normal substrate to overgrow adjacent moss, etc.

The chemical tests listed should be made on the surface of the lichen unless otherwise stated, + or – refers to all species in that group that are included in the book. The absence of an entry means that the test is unimportant or variable.

GROUP KEY

The first part of the key (1 to 7) covers the basic lichen forms. A decision has to be made as to which group a specimen to be identified belongs. These entries terminate in a letter (A to D or T) indicating the section of the main key that should be used. If an entry terminates in a figure (8,9 or 10) refer to this number in this group key. Here a further decision is required to provide the letter indicating the section of the main key that should be used.

MAIN KEY

A number of genera resemble those of a different group. In these cases the genus will key-out in both groups. The symbol ! after the name indicates that this genus does not taxonomically belong in that group.

The additional notes at the end of each entry refers to all members of that genus included in the book, but are not necessarily exclusive to that entry.

In most cases it should be possible to key-out a specimen to its genus but if due to lack of spores, etc., it can only be reduced to two or three possible genera, the details and photographs of each of these genera should be consulted in the main text. This should enable the user to determine the genus.

SPORE TYPES

SIMPLE   ONE SEPTATE   POLARILOCULAR   MULTISEPTATE   MURIFORM

GROUP KEY

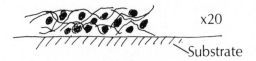

x20

Substrate

x5

1. LEPROSE   Consisting of a more or less diffuse powdery mass (or in this key, crustose but entirely covered in soredia)   *A*

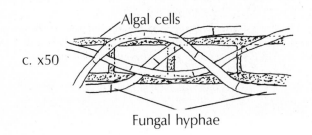

Algal cells

c. x50

Fungal hyphae

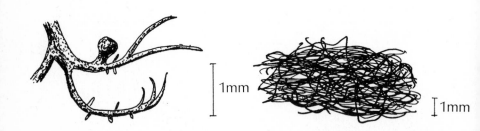

1mm

1mm

2. FILAMENTOUS   Very fine, soft hair-like or gathered into a felt-like mat of fine filaments. Fungal hyphae enveloping the algal filaments or chains. (If longer than 3cm, see 7)   *B*

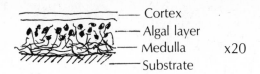

Cortex
Algal layer
Medulla   x20
Substrate

3. *CRUSTOSE*   Forming a crust which usually can only be removed with part of the substrate. Thallus in some cases thin or inside the substrate with only the apothecia showing at the surface.

Fruiting bodies present   8

or   Not fertile but with delimited soralia, isidia, or white pruinose, pycnidia   T

4. *PLACODIOID*   Crustose but appearing lobed towards the margin. Usually can only be removed with part of the substrate   C

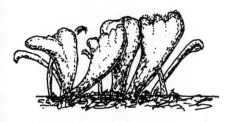

x10

5. *SQUAMULOSE*   Consisting of small (to c. 1cm long) leaf-like squamules, crustose at the base, often overlapping and forming mats. Fruiting bodies often podetia   D

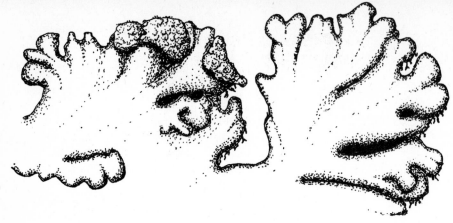

6. *FOLIOSE*   Flattened and leaf-like, often large. Distinctly dorsiventral species belong here (excluding squamulose). May be thin and papery when dry, swelling considerably when wet, Can usually be removed without part of the substrate, may be attached by rhizinae   9

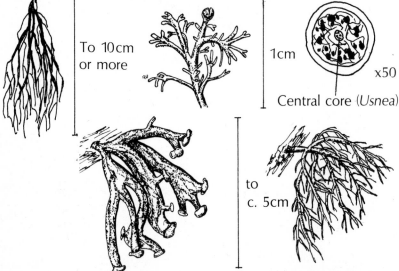

To 10 cm or more

1cm

x50

Central core (*Usnea*)

to c. 5cm

7. *FRUTICOSE*   Radially symmetrical, coarse, lacking a distinct upper and lower surface, branches rounded or flattened. (If dorsiventral go to 9). Attached to the substrate at one point only, or unattached. Algal layer surrounds the medulla, there is a central core in Usnea   10

8. CRUSTOSE
FRUITING BODIES

(i) Stalked   To 5mm high, indian-club or golf-tee shaped, lacking algal cells in the stalk

E

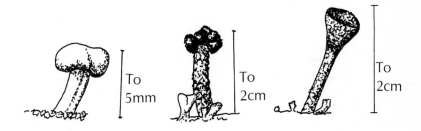

To 5mm

To 2cm

To 2cm

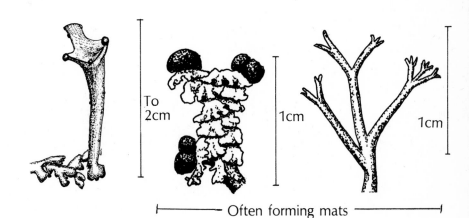

To 2cm

1cm

1cm

⊢——— Often forming mats ———⊣

(ii) Podetia or mushroom-shaped   Apothecia borne on hollow or solid stalks (podetia or pseudopodetia), or like small mushrooms to 5mm tall

F

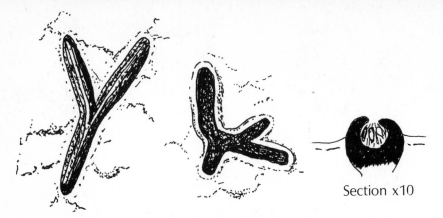

Section x10

(iii) Lirellate   Fruiting bodies more than twice as long as wide, often with black carbonaceous margins   G

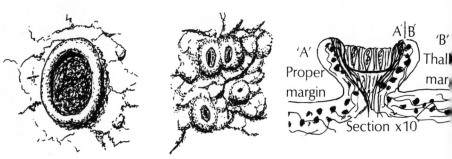

'A'
Proper
margin

A' B'

'B'
Thall
mar;

Section x10

(iv) Lecanorine   Apothecia disc-shaped, with a margin containing algal cells. The margin is usually of the same colour as the thallus (at least when young); sometimes sunk into the thallus when it may be confused with (v)   H

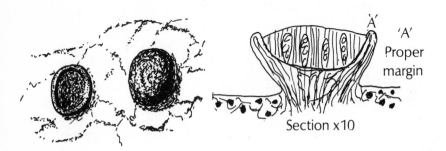

'A'
Proper
margin

Section x10

(v) Lecideine   Apothecia disc-shaped, but lacking the thalline margin found in species in group H   I

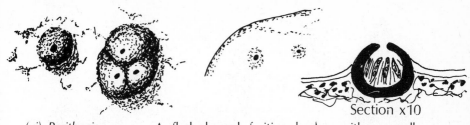

Section x10

| (vi) Perithecia | A flask-shaped fruiting body with a small opening at the tip, often cone shaped, superficial or may be immersed in the thallus or substrate; sometimes united in compact groups | J |

Section x10

| (vii) Arthonioid | Apothecia poorly delimited and lack a true margin often flat and irregular in outline and not in groups E-J | K |

9 (i)	Thallus and apothecia orange	L
(ii)	Thallus inflated	M
(iii)	Thallus attached only at the centre or at a single basal holdfast	N
(iv)	Lower surface tomentose	O
(v)	Not in groups L-O and attached to the substrate by rhizinae	P
(vi)	Not in groups L-O and attached to the substrate either directly or by adhesive pads	Q

| 10 (i) | Thallus hollow or orange | R |
| (ii) | Thallus solid, not orange | S |

Abreviations used in sections A—S of the main key

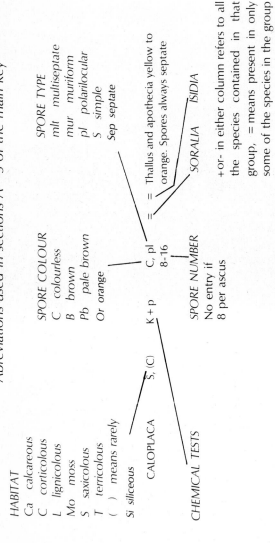

HABITAT
Ca calcareous
C   corticolous
L   lignicolous
Mo moss
S   saxicolous
T   terricolous
( ) means rarely
Si siliceous

SPORE COLOUR
C   colourless
B   brown
Pb pale brown
Or orange

SPORE TYPE
mlt multiseptate
mur muriform
pl   polarilocular
S   simple
Sep septate

= = Thallus and apothecia yellow to orange. Spores always septate

+or- in either column refers to all the species contained in that group, = means present in only some of the species in the group

CALOPLACA S, (C) K + p C, pl 8-16 SORALIA ISIDIA

SPORE NUMBER
No entry if
8 per ascus

CHEMICAL TESTS

T. CRUSTOSE. Not fertile and with delimited soralia or with isidia

GENUS OR SPECIES	THALLUS COLOUR	HABITAT	REACTIONS	NOTES
OCHROLECHIA androgyna	Grey	Trees and moss	C + o	Pale yellow, globose soralia

Anaptychia ciliaris

Arthonia tumidula

Catillaria sphaeroides

Baeomyces rufus

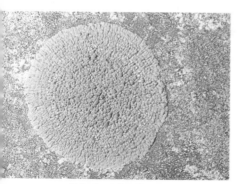

Caloplaca heppiana

Caloplaca saxicola

Caloplaca thallincola

Cladonia chlorophaea

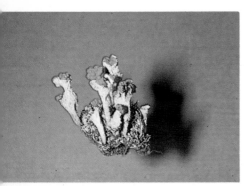

Cladonia coccifera

Cladonia rangiformis

Cladonia uncialis
Cetraria islandica

Diploschistes scruposus

Evernia prunastri

Gyalectina carneolutea

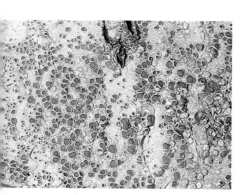

Lecanora chlarotera

Lecanora intricata
var. soralifera

Lecanora muralis

Huilia albocaerulescens

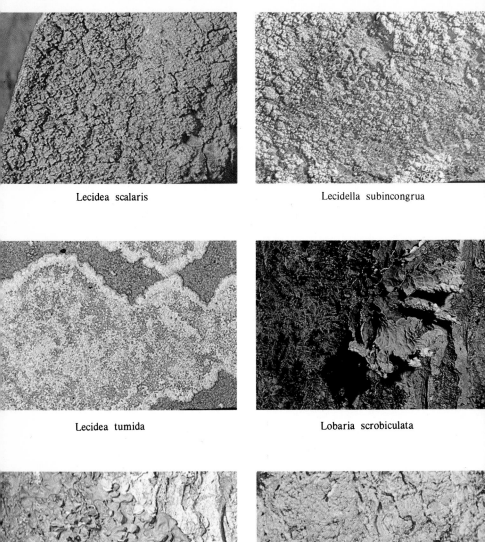

Lecidea scalaris

Lecidella subincongrua

Lecidea tumida

Lobaria scrobiculata

Nephroma laevigatum

Ochrolechia androgyna

MAIN KEY

GENUS OR SPECIES	HABITAT	REACT.	SPORES	Sor.	Is.	NOTES

A. LEPROSE

(Note, a number of other species often form sorediate crusts)

GENUS OR SPECIES	HABITAT	REACT.	SPORES	Sor.	Is.	NOTES
LEPRARIA	All	K-/fy				Some species almost lobate marginally
LEPROPLACA	Ca S	K+p				Thallus yellow (one species more or less marginally lobate)
SCHISMATOMMA!	C,	K-/fy				White to mauve-grey sorediate crust on rough bark
LECIDEA lucida!	S	Neg				Yellow-green. Found on damp walls and rocks
LECANORA expallens!	C, L	K-,C+o				Yellow to yellowish-grey.Very common especially on trees and fences (see also *Lecidea quernea*)
DIRINA!	S	C+r				Soft pinkish-grey, orange when scratched, more or less maritime

B. FILAMENTOUS

GENUS OR SPECIES	HABITAT	REACT.	SPORES	Sor.	Is.	NOTES
LICHINA!	S	Neg	C, S	-	-	Dark brown to black, shrubby, to 1 cm high. Found around H.W.M. Apothecia spherical at branch tips
EPHEBE lanata	S		C, 1(2)sep	-	-	Forms soft mats to c.1cm across on damp rocks. Filiments much divided with fine points
ALECTORIA!	S, C		PB, S	=	-	Forms rather wiry brown mats or festoons
CYSTOCOLEUS niger	SiS			-	-	Black and felted, on shaded rock. Fungal hyphae contorted and surrounding algal strands
RACODIUM rupestre	Si S			-	-	As *Cystocoleus* but with fungal hyphae straight and parallel

C. PLACODIOID

GENUS OR SPECIES	HABITAT	REACT.	SPORES	Sor.	Is.	NOTES
LECANORA muralis	S	Neg	C, S	-	-	Greenish-grey lobes with white edges. Common on man-made substrates
PLACOPSIS gelida	Si S	K + y C + r	C, S	+	-	Mainly upland. Pink-brown cephalodia, reddish discs
FULGENSIA	Ca T	K + p	C, S	-	-	Thallus egg-yellow. Apothecia common, red. Spores usually simple
CANDELARIELLA medians	Ca S	K-	C, S	-	-	Yellow lobes, (greyish in centre). Apothecia rare, yellow
CALOPLACA	S, (C)	K + p	C, pl 8-16	=	=	Thallus and apothecia yellow to orange. Spores always septate
SOLENOPSORA candicans	Ca S	K-,P-	C, 1sep	-	-	Chalk-white. Disc brownish-black and pruinose. On hard maritime limestone rocks
BUELLIA canescens	S, C	K + y	B, 1sep	+	-	Nutrient enriched substrates. White pruinose lobes. Apothecia rare except in South
PHYSCIA!	S, C		B, 1-pl	=	-	Discs black. Lobes narrow often pruinose and/or pseudocyphellate. With care the lobate structure can normally be traced to the centre of the thallus

D. SQUAMULOSE

GENUS OR SPECIES	HABITAT	REACT.	SPORES	Sor.	Is.	NOTES
CLADONIA	C, T			=	-	Green yellowish-green or grey mats of squamules, often erect and overlapping and bearing hollow podetia
NORMANDINA pulchella	Mo, L	Neg		+	-	Green oyster shell-shaped with raised slightly paler, sometimes sorediate margins. To 3mm across. Clean air
CORISCIUM viride	T			-	-	Blue-green, adpressed, oyster shell-shaped. On peat. Fruits a mushroom (Omphalina)

GENUS OR SPECIES	HABITAT	REACT.	SPORES	Sor.	Is.	NOTES
LECIDEA	C, L, S		C, S	=	-	With upper and lower cortex. Fruits apothecia, lacking a thalline margin
DERMATO-CARPON	S, T	Neg	S, C	-	-	Fixed by central holdfast or rhizinae. Fruits immersed, reddish perithecia
PARMELIELLA	C, S		C, S-1sep	-	=	Apothecia reddish, lecideine. Lower surface a dark felted hypothallus
PANNARIA	C, S		C, S	-	-	Apothecia lecanorine. Lower surface sometimes a dark felted hypothallus
SQUAMARINA	Ca T, S		C, S	-	-	Grey-brown with pruinose edges. Apothecia lecanorine, discs brown
PSOROMA hypnorum	C, S, T	Neg	C, S	-	-	Green to orange-brown, with rhizinae. In damp shade in upland areas. Discs red-brown
ACAROSPORA	S		C, S 50 +	-	-	Areolate to squamulose. Apothecia often immersed and indistinct
TONINIA	Ca T, S		C, 1-3sep	-	-	Lobes very convex, usually grey and very pruinose. Apothecia lecideine, large, black and globose. Discs often pruinose

E. Pin-stalked or indian-club shaped

GENUS OR SPECIES	HABITAT	REACT.	SPORES	Sor.	Is.	NOTES
CONIOCYBE furfuracea	S, L, T		Or, S	+	-	Yellow-green thallus on soil or in dry tree cracks. Stalks yellow, to 4mm. Spores minute
CHAENOTHECA ferruginea	C	K-	B, S	+	-	Soredia grey-yellow to red. Stalks to 3mm. In bark cracks
STENOCYBE	C	Neg	B, 1-3sep	-	-	Fruits indian-club shaped, to 3mm. Smooth bark, usually holly or alder
CALICIUM	C	Neg	B, 1sep	-	-	Stalks to 2mm. Spores constricted at septum

F. Podetia, pseudopodetia or mushroom-shaped

GENUS OR SPECIES	HABITAT	REACT.	SPORES	Sor.	Is.	NOTES
BAEOMYCES	S, T	K + y	C, S-1sep	-	-	Apothecia pink to brown, on stalks, mushroom-shaped
PILOPHORUS strumaticus	Si S	K + y	C, S	+	-	Mushroom–shaped black apothecia rare, stalked soralia common. On upland shaded moist rocks
THAMNOLIA vermicularis	T	K + y P + y		-	-	Pure white, unbranched, pointed tubes. Found above c.2000 ft. Fruits unknown
LEPROCAULON microscopicum	Ca T, S	K-, KC + y		+	-	Yellow-green, to 3mm high. Fimbriate becoming sorediate
PYCNOTHELIA papillaria	Peat	K + y	C, S	-	-	Podetia to 1.5cm high, hollow, grey-brown, darker tips, unbranched cylindrical, often densely packed
CLADONIA	All		C, S-1sep	+	-	Red or brown apothecia. Podetia hollow, often much branched and interwoven. Basal squamules may form mat
STEREO-CAULON	Si S, Mo	K + y	C, 3-7sep	-	-	Podetia solid, often with dark cephalodia. Branchlets flattened
SPHAERO-PHORUS	T, S		B, S	-	-	Podetia solid. Apothecia rare, globose at tips, spores in a powdery mass. Branchlets rounded

G. Lirellate

GENUS OR SPECIES	HABITAT	REACT.	SPORES	Sor.	Is.	NOTES
XYLOGRAPHA abietina	L	Neg	C, S	-	-	Lirellae brown
GRAPHIS	C	Neg	C, mlt	-	-	Emergent and often furrowed margins, lirellae to 2cm long
E NTEROGRAPHA!	C, (S)	Neg	C, mlt	-	-	Perithecia minute, immersed and in lines so as to appear lirellate. Black prothallus

GENUS OR SPECIES	HABITAT	REACT.	SPORES	Sor.	Is.	NOTES
OPEGRAPHA	C, S	Neg	C ,3 + sep	-	-	Lirellae to 5mm long
ARTHONIA!	C	Neg	C, 3sep	-	-	Brownish thallus. Apothecia irregular in shape, often stellate to 2mm long. Spores clavate
GRAPHINA	C	Neg	C, mur	-	-	Usually with flat margins, disc often leprose
PHAEOGRAPHIS	C	K + y-r/-	B, mlt	-	-	Discs often flat and pruinose

H. Lecanorine
Spores colourless, simple

GENUS OR SPECIES	HABITAT	REACT.	SPORES	Sor.	Is.	NOTES
LECANORA	C, S,L		C,S	=	-	Thallus grey, brownish or yellowish – green, not yellow. Apothecia sessile or immersed
CANDELARIELLA	S, C, L	K-	C, S 8-32	-	-	Thallus and apothecia lemon or mustard – yellow. Spores may rarely appear septate
OCHROLECHIA	S, C	C + /-	C, S 2-8	=	-	Thallus white or grey often warted. Spores very large. Discs pinkish but often pruinose
PERTUSARIA	S, C		C, S 1-8	=	=	Apothecia often more or less innate or in warts. Spores very large. Margin of thallus often limited by concentric rings
PLACOPSIS gelida!	Si S	K + y C + r	C, S	+	-	Upland species with wart-like pink to brown cephalodia
ACAROSPORA	S		C, S 50 +	-	-	Areolate to squamulose

Spores polarilocular

GENUS OR SPECIES	HABITAT	REACT.	SPORES	Sor.	Is.	NOTES
CALOPLACA	S, C	K + p/-	C, Pl 8-16	=	=	Thallus yellow, orange, grey or white. Apothecia mainly orange or red K + p., apothecia sometimes black
RINODINA	C, S		B, Pl-3sep	-	-	Mainly grey or greenish-grey thallus and black discs

GENUS OR SPECIES	HABITAT	REACT.	SPORES	Sor.	Is.	NOTES

Spores septate

GENUS OR SPECIES	HABITAT	REACT.	SPORES	Sor.	Is.	NOTES
ICMADOPHILA	T	K + y	C, 1-3sep	-	-	Apothecia flesh–pink swollen and becoming convex K + o. Thallus whitish-green. Found on peat, rarely rotting wood
LECANIA	S, C	Neg	C, 1-3sep 8-16	=	-	Apothecia fawn to black minute to small, becoming very convex
HAEMATOMMA	S, C	K + y	C, 3-8sep	+	-	Discs blood–red and K + p. Thallus usually yellowish
CYPHELIUM	L, C	Neg	B, 1sep	-	-	Apothecia irregular in outline, black. Spores in powdery mass which leaves a sooty mark on the finger

Spores muriform (these species are not strictly lecanorine)

GENUS OR SPECIES	HABITAT	REACT.	SPORES	Sor.	Is.	NOTES
PHLYCTIS	C	K + y/r	C, mur 2	=	-	Thallus white to grey, apothecia immersed with whitish margins
THELOTREMA lepadinum	C	Neg	C-B mlt/mur	-	-	Apothecia with a visible inner margin, 'barnacle-like'
DIPLOSCHISTES	C	C + r	B mlt/mur	=	-	Discs immersed, at least when young

I. Lecideine
Spores colourless, simple

GENUS OR SPECIES	HABITAT	REACT.	SPORES	Sor.	Is.	NOTES
LECIDEA LECIDELLA	All		C, S	=	-	Usually dark-coloured discs
MYCOBLASTUS sanguinarius	S, Mo	K + y	S 1-3	-	-	Medulla with red patches, spores very large with many nuclei
XYLOGRAPHA abietina	L	Neg	C, S	-	-	Apothecia dark-brown and oval becoming lirellate in appearance
SARCOGYNE	S	Neg	C, S 50 +	-	-	Often endolithic, discs chestnut to black, often with convoluted margins
PROTO-BLASTENIA	Ca S	Ap. K + p	C, S	-	-	Apothecia convex, orange, (black and K- in some species not included in this book)

Spores colourless, septate to muriform

GENUS OR SPECIES	HABITAT	REACT.	SPORES	Sor.	Is.	NOTES
CATILLARIA	C, S		C, 1sep	=	-	Spores are often slightly cres-cent-shaped. Apothecia black or brown
LECANIA!	S, C	Neg	C, 1-3sep 8-16	=	-	Apothecia fawn to black, very small, becoming convex. Actually Lecanorine
DIMERELLA	C, Mo	K-	C, 1sep	-	-	Thallus grey or evanescent. Apothecia translucent flesh-colour or yellow-orange
LECANACTIS	C		C, 3-7sep	-	-	Shaded rough bark. Carbonaceous sometimes pruinose apothecia. Pycnidia C + r in one species
PACHYPHIALE	C	Neg	C, mlt	-	-	Apothecia to 0.75mm reddish-brown, the smooth proper margin gives a 'wine-gum' appearance. Found on rough-barked deciduous trees
GYALECTINA	C,(Ca S)	Neg	C, 3sep 8-16	-	-	Mainly on shaded ash and elm. Apothecia translucent yellow with dentate margins
GYALECTA	C, S	Neg	C, mlt/mur	-	-	Apothecia orange or yellow with dentate margins
PETRACTIS clausa	Hard Ca S	Neg	C, 3sep +	-	-	Pale orange disc 0.5mm, with whitish toothed margins
BACIDIA	C, S		C 3-mlt	-	=.	Apothecia often convex and rubbery when wet
TONINIA	Ca S, T		C, 1-3sep	-	-	Often with deep 'roots', pruinose. Discs black, convex, often pruinose
DIRINA	Ca S	C + r	C, 3-8sep	=		Thallus orange when scratched in fresh material

GENUS OR SPECIES	HABITAT	REACT.	SPORES	Sor.	ls.	NOTES
RHIZOCARPON	S		C, 1-mlt usl mur 2-8	-	-	Thallus areolate with a black prothallus evident as lines giving the margin a mosaic-like appearance. Apothecia dark brown or black, immersed
PLACYNTHIUM nigrum	Hard Ca S	Neg	C, 1-3sep	-	-	Crust of minute coralloid granules, blue-black prothallus

Spores brown, septate to muriform

BUELLIA	S, C		B, 1-3sep to = mur 4-8		-	Discs black
S C L E R O - PHYTON circumscriptum	S	K + y	B, 5-7sep	=	-	Under overhangs. Orange when scratched. Apothecia in lines

J. Perithecia (sometimes immersed)

VERRUCARIA	S		C S	-	-	Found mainly around H.W.M. or in streams or on calcareous substrates
ARTHOPYRENIA	S, C		C, 1sep	-	-	Spores clavate. Found on smooth bark or calc. substrates
PORINA	C, S		C, 1-mlt	-	-	Perithecia often grouped. Thallus grey to green-brown. Spores sometimes slightly muriform
E N T E R O - GRAPHA	C, (S)	Neg	C, mlt	-	-	Perithecia minute, immersed and in lines so as to appear lirellate. Black prothallus
THELIDIUM	Ca S		C-B, 1-3sep	-	-	Spores often muriform, slightly clavate. Thallus white to grey or evanescent
POLYBLASTIA	S, T		C-B, mur 2-8	-	-	Thallus often immersed. Perithecia simple or grouped
PYRENULA	C		B, 1-3sep	--	-	On smooth bark, mosaic forming. Spores loculate. Thallus waxy with white flecks

GENUS OR SPECIES	HABITAT	REACT.	SPORES	Sor.	Is.	NOTES
STAUROTHELE fissa	S	Neg	B, mur 2	-	-	Thallus green-grey to brown. On rocks in streams. Perithecia with hymenial algae
TOMASELLIA gelatinosa	C	Neg	C- *Pb* 1-3sep	-	-	Perithecia grouped in black stroma. Found mainly on hazel

K. Arthonioid

ARTHONIA	C	neg	C, 1-3sep	-	-	Spores slightly clavate. Apothecia often stellate, reddish orange or black, up to c.3mm across

FOLIOSE

L. Thallus and apothecia orange

XANTHORIA	C, S	K + p	C, p l	-	=	Lobes usually wider than 1mm. Nutrient rich sites
CANDELARIA concolor	C, S	K-	C, S 8 +	+	+	Lobes to 1mm wide, erect. Sorediate or isidiate tips

M. Thallus inflated

HYPOGYMNIA	C, S	K + y med KC + r	C, S	+	-	Attached by adhesive pads. Common even in moderate pollution. Upper surface not perforated by small holes
MENEGAZZIA	C, S	K + y med P + o	C, S 2-4	+	-	Upper surface perforated by small, neat circular holes

N. Thallus attached only at the centre or by single basal holdfast

EVERNIA prunastri	C, S, T,	K + y	S, C	+	-	Upper surface yellowish-green, lower surface white. Lobes less than 10mm wide with feint net-like white lines
UMBILICARIA	S		C-B S-Mur 1-8	-	=	Thallus papery when dry. Apothecia often convoluted

GENUS OR SPECIES	HABITAT	REACT.	SPORES	Sor.	Is.	NOTES
PSEUDEVERNIA furfuracea	Si S, C, L	K + y	C, S	-	+	Looks fruticose. Upper surface grey, undersurface black or white. Apothecia very rare
D E R M A T O - CARPON	S	Neg	C, S	-	-	Thallus grey or brown. Perithecia immersed with brown ostioles visible
PHYSCIA	C, S	K + y	C, 1sep	=	-	Lobes less than 2mm wide often with long marginal cilia
ANAPTYCHIA ciliaris	C, S	Neg	B, 1sep	-	-	Lobes to 4mm wide and 4cm long with long marginal cilia

O. Lower surface tomentose

GENUS OR SPECIES	HABITAT	REACT.	SPORES	Sor.	Is.	NOTES
STICTA	C, S		C, 1-3sep	=	=	Lower surface with neat white circular depressions (cyphellae). Not usually fertile
LOBARIA	C, S		C-B, 1-9sep	=	=	Large and spreading. No cyphellae on lower surface. Found in unpolluted regions in old forested areas
PELTIGERA	C, S		C, Mlt (c.8)	=	=	Apothecia red-brown on upper surface of lobe tips. Thallus large and spreading
P S E U D O - CYPHELLARIA	C, S		B, 1-3sep	+	-	Apothcia rare. Soralia mauve-grey or greenish-yellow. Lower surface with distinct pseudocyphellae. Oceanic, Western
SOLORINA	T, S	K + v/-	B, 1sep 2-8	-	-	Apothecia innate, lecideine, reddish. Lower surface with rhizinae
UMBILICARIA polyrrhiza!	Si S	C + r	C, S 1-8	-	-	Lower surface a dense mass of fine, black, forked rhizinae

P. Not in groups L-O and attached to the substrate by rhizinae

GENUS OR SPECIES	HABITAT	REACT.	SPORES	Sor.	Is	NOTES
PARMELIA	C, S	most K + y	C, S 2-8	=	=	Thallus often large and spreading. Lower surface with rhizinae
PLATISMATIA glauca	C, Si S	K + y	C, S	+	=	Erect with only very few coarse rhizinae. Lobes thin and papery often with small white flecks on the upper surface. Apothecia rare
CETRARIA	C, S		C, S	=	-	Lobes often long and erect, often only a few coarse rhizinae present
PARMELIOPSIS	C, (S)	C-	C, S	=	=	Like a small Parmelia, closely adpressed to the substrate. Apothecia rare
UMBILICARIA polyrrhiza!	S	C + r	C, S	-	-	Upper surface copper-brown when dry, green-brown when wet. Lower surface a dense mat of fine black rhizinae
LEPTOGIUM	S, C, T	Neg	C, 3 sep -mur 4-8	-	=	Thin and papery and blue-grey when dry, swollen, green or brown when wet. Rhizinae fine or absent. Apothecia with red-brown discs
PELTIGERA	C, S		C- Pb 3-mlt	=	=	Usually large and loosely attached, often by large rhizinae. Apothecia on upper surface of lobe tips
SOLORINA	T		B, 1-3sep 2-8	-	-	Apothecia innate in upper surface, reddish, lecideine
PHYSCIA	C, S		B, 1sep	=	=	Narrow lobes often with white pseudocyphellae and/or marginal cilia. Discs dark but often pruinose
PHYSCIOPSIS adglutinata	C, Si S	Med K-	B, 1sep	+	-	Thallus up to 1.5cm diam. lobes under 1.5 mm wide. Surface splits to give greenish soralia
ANAPTYCHIA fusca	S	K-	B, 1sep	-	-	Large brown thallus, bleaches with the aplication of C. Maritime

Q. *Attached to the substrate directly or by adhesive pads*

GENUS OR SPECIES	HABITAT	REACT.	SPORES	Sor.	Is.	NOTES
PLATISMATIA glauca	C, Si S	K + y	C, S	+	+	Erect with sorediate/isidiate margins, lobes thin and papery often with white flecks on upper surface. Apothecia rare, with brown discs
CAVERNULARIA hultenii	C	K + y	C, S	+	-	Grey above with deep depressions on the dark lower surface. Lobes to 1mm wide with sorediate tips. Found in Scotland
DERMATOCARPON	S	Neg	C, S	-	-	Perithecia immersed with brown ostioles visible
NEPHROMA	C, S		C, 3-mlt	=	-	Apothecia on lower surface of lobe tips. Medulla yellow except in rare species
LEPTOGIUM	C, S, T	Neg	C, 3-mur 6-8	-	=	Thin and papery, grey when dry, swollen, brown or green when wet. Discs red-brown
COLLEMA	C, S, T	Neg	C, mlt/mur	-	=	Thin and papery, black when dry, very swollen gelatinous greenish-black when wet. Discs red-brown

FRUTICOSE

R. *Thallus hollow or orange*

GENUS OR SPECIES	HABITAT	REACT.	SPORES	Sor.	Is.	NOTES
TELOSCHISTES	C, S	K + c	C, pl	=	-	Thallus greenish-orange to orange. More or less maritime
CLADONIA	T		C, S-1sep	=	-	Tangled mat of greyish or yellowish-green hollow branches, or hollow podetia that often grow from basal squamules
THAMNOLIA vermicularis	T	K + y P + y		-	-	White or yellowish sparsely branched tubes. Found above c.900m on acid heathland

S. *Thallus solid not orange*

GENUS OR SPECIES	HABITAT	REACT.	SPORES	Sor.	Is.	NOTES
LICHINA	S	Neg	C, S	-	-	Dark–brown to black, shrubby, to 1cm high. Found around H.W.M. Apothecia spherical, at branch tips
CORNICULARIA	T, S	Neg (C + r)	C, S	-	-	Glossy–brown, spiky mats on soil; or erect, matt and brown-black, found on exposed boulders
EVERNIA prunastri!	C, S, T,	K + y	S, C	+	-	Upper surface yellowish-green, lower surface white. Lobes less than 10mm wide with feint net-like lines
PSEUDEVERNIA furfuracea!	Si S, C, L,	K + y	C, S	-	+	Upper surface grey, under surface black or white. Apothecia very rare
USNEA	C, S, L		C, S	=	=	Branches round with a tough elastic central core. Bushy to pendent. Attached by a single often blackened holdfast
RAMALINA	C, S	C-	S, 1sep	=	-	Fawn to green-grey. More or less flattened, with no central core
STEREOCAULON	Si S, L	K + y	C, 3-7sep	-	-	Branchlets pale grey, coralloid, small and flattened. Cephalodia often present. Found on heathland and acid rocks
ROCCELLA	S	C + r	S, mlt	+	-	Cortex or soralia C + r. Thallus bluish-grey. Apothecia very rare. Found in South and West in maritime situations
ALECTORIA	C, S		PB, S 2-8	=	-	Greenish-yellow to black. No central core. Erect tufts, prostrate or pendent, round or flattened
SPHAEROPHORUS	S, T, (C)		B, S	-	-	Bushy, branchlets terete, apothecia globose at branch tips

T. CRUSTOSE. *Not fertile and with delimited soralia or with isidia*

ISIDIATE

GENUS OR SPECIES	THALLUS COLOUR	HABITAT	REACTIONS	NOTES
PERTUSARIA coccodes	Grey	Trees	Medulla K + y	Grey to brown isidia
P. corallina	Pale grey	Rocks	K + y	Isidia concolorous (If thallus is K + r then *P. pseudocorallina*)
P. flavida	Yellow-green	Trees	C + o	Dense massed isidia, (see *P. flavida* if isidia are eroded)
OCHROLECHIA yasudae	Grey	Old trees	Isidia C + o	Dense cylindrical isidia

SOREDIATE
On rocks or soil, sometimes on moss
Cortex or soralia C + orange to red

GENUS OR SPECIES	THALLUS COLOUR	HABITAT	REACTIONS	NOTES
LECIDEA granulosa	Grey-yellow	Soil or stumps	C + r	Green-grey, yellow or reddish soralia
OCHROLECHIA androgyna	Grey	Rocks	C + o	Pale yellow, globose soralia
PERTUSARIA lactea	Grey	Rocks	Soralia C + r	Punctiform, concolorous soralia
LECIDEA scabra	Green-grey	Rock	C + o	Greenish-grey punctiform soralia. Found on exposed acid rock
DIRINA stenhammarii	Warm grey	Calc. rocks	C + r	Soralia concolorous, becoming confluent. Thallus scratches orange

GENUS OR SPECIES	THALLUS COLOUR	HABITAT	REACTIONS	NOTES

Cortex and soralia C−

GENUS OR SPECIES	THALLUS COLOUR	HABITAT	REACTIONS	NOTES
LECIDIA cinnabarina	Grey	Trees	Soralia P + r	Yellowish, oval soralia
L. tumida	Grey	Acid rocks		Blue-grey punctiform soralia
LECANIA erysibe	Grey	Calc. rock		Small yellow-green punctiform soralia. Pollution tolerant

Found on trees, wood or moss
Cortex or soralia C + orange or red

GENUS OR SPECIES	THALLUS COLOUR	HABITAT	REACTIONS	NOTES
OCHROLECHIA androgyna	Grey	Trees and moss	C + o	Pale yellow, globose soralia. Thallus warted
O. inversa	Grey	Trees	C + o	Yellow-green soralia becoming confluent
PERTUSARIA hemisphaerica	Grey	Trees	C + rose	White delimited soralia
LECANORA expallens	Yellowish-green	Trees and fences	K + y, C + o	Concolorous soralia that become confluent
LECIDELLA eleochroma	Greenish-grey	Trees	Soralia C + o	Small yellow-green punctiform soralia

Cortex and soralia C−

GENUS OR SPECIES	THALLUS COLOUR	HABITAT	REACTIONS	NOTES
PERTUSARIA amara	Grey	Trees (rocks)	Soralia KC + v	White, delimited soralia with a bitter taste
P. albescens	Grey	Trees rocks	Soralia KC−	White, delimited soralia with a mild taste
P. multipuncta	Grey	Trees	K + y, P + y	White large soralia, which actually cover the apothecia
HAEMATOMMA elatinum	Grey	Trees	K + y, P + y	Globose, yellow-green soralia that become confluent
CATILLARIA lightfootii	Greenish-grey	Trees	Soralia P + y(−)	Concolorous, granular soralia

GENUS OR SPECIES	THALLUS COLOUR	HABITAT	REACTIONS	NOTES
CHAENOTHECA ferruginea	Fawn to red	Dry bark	Soralia K + r	Reddish slightly sorediate patches
LECANORA jamesii	grey	Smooth bark	Soralia K + y(−)	Yellow-green, small, punctiform soralia
PHLYCTIS argena	Pale grey	Trees	Soralia K + o	Soralia thin and in patches over the thallus
SCHISMATOMMA species	White to grey	Trees		Soralia concolorous and becoming confluent

White pruinose pycnidia with the superficial appearance of soralia

| LECANACTIS abietina | Warm grey | Rough bark | Pynidia C + r | If pycnidia are C− see *Opegrapha vermicellifera* |

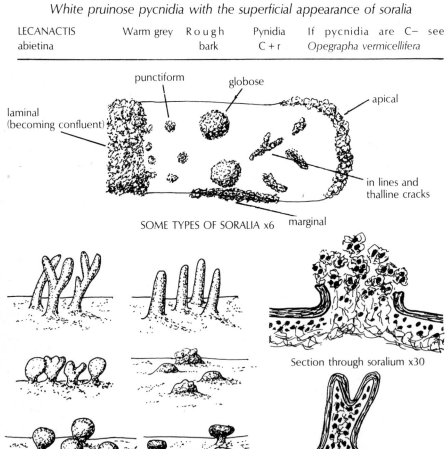

SOME TYPES OF SORALIA x6

punctiform
globose
apical
laminal (becoming confluent)
in lines and thalline cracks
marginal

SOME TYPES OF ISIDIA x20

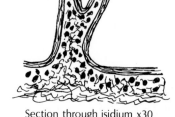

Section through soralium x30

Section through isidium x30

Ochrolechia tartarea

Parmelia britannica

Parmelia conspersa

Parmelia exasperata

Parmelia mougeotii

Parmelia omphalodes

Parmelia saxatilis

Parmelia subrudecta

Peltigera canina

Peltigera horizontalis

Pertusaria albescens
Pertusaria pertusa

Pertusaria corallina
Pertusaria pseudocorallina

Pertusaria pertusa

Phaeographis dendritica

Physcia orbicularis

Physciopsis adglutinata

Ramalina cuspidata

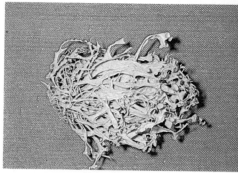

Ramalina fraxinea

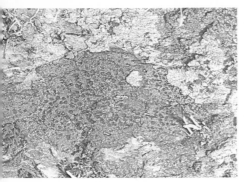

Rhizocarpon constrictum

Thelotrema lepadinum

Umbilicaria polyrrhiza

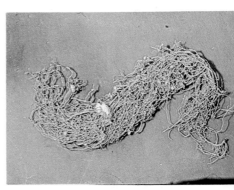

Usnea ceratina

Xanthoria parietina

Xanthoria polycarpa
Physcia tenella

ACAROSPORACEAE The genera contained in the Acarosporaceae have the smallest spores to be found in British lichens. Most species found with asci containing several hundred very small colourless simple spores belong to this family.

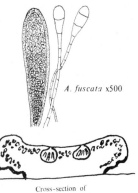

A. fuscata x500

Cross-section of
A. fuscata

ACAROSPORA Thallus appears crustose (it does in fact consist of small squamules), areolate. Phycobiont green. The species are mainly rare except for the following.

Acarospora fuscata Thallus matt yellow-brown to dark reddish–brown, thick with angular areolae that are raised at the edges like dried mud. Apothecia innate and dark reddish–brown, one or several to an areole.
C + red (or-).
Habitat. A common species on nutrient-rich hard siliceous rocks and also in other areas where there are suitable churchyards or monuments. It appears to reach its best development in slightly polluted areas where it is also commonest.

A. fuscata x8

1

A. smaragdula Thallus creamy-brown, may be distinguished from *A. fuscata* by the flat to convex squamules that are often very scattered and by the C− and K + red reaction (sometimes hard to obtain).

Habitat. Fairly common on metal-rich siliceous rock in upland coastal areas.

A. smaragdula x6

ALECTORIA The name is thought to be derived from the Greek for "unwedded" due to the scarcity of fruiting bodies. It has been said to improve the colour of hair, black hair from the darker species and blonde from the yellow species. The corticolous species form an important food for the reindeer and caribou when the ground is snow-covered and also as food for man in *A. fremontii* pancakes. Thallus fruticose, erect, pendent or prostrate. Branches terete up to 2mm diam becoming flattened and expanded in some species. Apothecia are very rare in the British species (they are more common in the Scottish Highlands). Spores 2-4 or 8 per ascus, simple, ellipsoid, colourless to brown. Medulla randomly orientated with no solid core. Soralia if present are delimited tuberculate (borne on outgrowths from the cortex) or fissural (formed in splits in the cortex). Phycobiont *Trebouxia*.

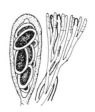

If Pd test is thought to be negative, it should be repeated on other parts of the thallus, especially the apices.

Species	Colour	Form	Habitat	Key Reactions	Pseudo-cyphellae	Soralia	Remarks
fuscescens	Matt–brown paler at base	Pendant or prostrate	Trees, fences rocks and soil	Cortex Pd + red(−)	−	+	Very common in Scotland
bicolor	Base black tips brown	Erect tufts	Mossy rocks and trees	Medulla in parts Pd + red	−	−	Abundant spinules
chalybeiformis	Brown to black	Prostrate	Rocks	Medulla Pd– Soralia Pd + r	−	−	Uplands
pubescens	Dark–brown	Prostrate mat	Rocks	All–	−	−	Fertile on high ground
sarmentosa subsp. sarmentosa	Greenish-yellow	Pendant	Rocks and trees	Medulla CK– KC– or + red	+	−	Very rare Scotland
sarmentosa subsp. vexillifera	Greenish-yellow	Prostrate dorsiventrally flattened	Arctic-alpine heathland	Medulla KC + or–,CK–	+	−	
subcana	Grey-green to pale brown	Pendant	Trees	Pd + orange to red	−	+	Northern and western
nigricans	Blackish tips pinkish base.	Erect	Arctic-alpine heathland	K + fy KC + red C + red	+	−	
ochroleuca	Greenish-yellow	Erect	Arctic-alpine heathland	Cort.KC + y Med CK + y,KC–	+	−	Rare Scottish Highlands
capillaris	Grey-green to brown	Pendant	Trees	K + y,KC + rose Pd + y–o	+ Very minute	±	Scottish Highlands

Note. Yellow species tend to be yellow-green in the field becoming yellow as the algae die.

3

Alectoria fuscescens [Bryoria fuscesens]
The commonest and most widespread species in Britain. Thallus prostrate or pendant, 5—15cm long. Branching mainly at acute angles. Branches terete, somewhat flattened at the axils of the main branches which are up to 0.5mm diam (sometimes more near the base in

var. *positiva*). Matt or with a very slight sheen, smokey green-brown to very dark brown, usually paler at the base. Soralia are frequently abundant and are of both tuberculate and fissural forms, sometimes spinulose.

Thallus K−, C−, KC−, P + red or P−. Soralia frequently give a stronger reaction.

Habitat. Common on trees, fences, posts and rocks.

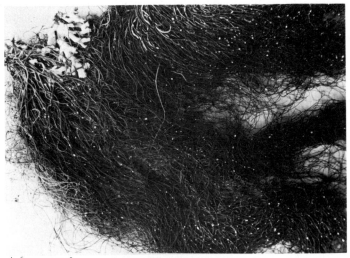

A. fuscescens x2

A. capillaris [Bryoria capillaris] Thallus similar in colour to *A. fuscescens* or paler. The base of the thallus frequently decays away. Apothecia are unknown in Britain. May be distinguished from *A. fuscescens* by the K + bright yellow, KC + red, Pd + o C + orange (−) reaction. Habitat. Chiefly confined to the old conifer forests in the Scottish Highlands.

A. capillaris x1.5

A. chalybeiformis [Bryoria chalybeiformis]

May be distinguished from *A. fuscescens* by the dark grey to black glossy thallus, the sparse branching towards the base with the wider main branches contorted and 0.5-2mm diam. Soralia sparse and tuberculate.

Thallus K−, C−, Pd − (+). Soralia Pd + r.

Habitat. Mossy rocks, soil, or the horizontal branches of trees in upland areas.

A. chalybeiformis x1.5

A. subcana [Bryoria subcana] Pendent branching frequently from the base at obtuse angles. Grey-green. Soralia tuberculate.

Thallus K−, KC−, C−, P + intensely orange-red. The stronger and more rapid Pd reaction together with the thallus colour helps to differentiate this species from *A. fuscescens*.

Habitat. Fairly rare on trees in upland areas.

A. subcana x1.5

A. bicolor [Bryoria bicolor] Erect, forming dense tufts usually 2-3cm tall. Branches terete 0.2—0.7mm diam. glossy. Green-grey at apices, brown-black at base. Numerous spiky spinules with constricted bases arise at right angles to the main stem. Soralia absent. Cortex K−, KC−, C−, P−. Medulla Pd + red at least in parts.

Habitat. Frequent on mosses on boulders and trees.

A. bicolor x4

A. pubescens [Pseudephebe pubescens]
Forms prostrate mats, usually radiating, rarely exceeding 1cm in height, branching frequently from the base, attached to the substrate over almost the whole of the thallus area. Branches up to 0.2mm diam. Dark brown to black often glossy, wiry. Fixed to the substrate  by hapters. Soralia absent. One of the few British species in which apothecia are common. Apothecia are mostly only found in specimens above about 600 metres and are dark grey or brown, up to 5mm diam, often with ciliate margins. Spores colourless, 8 per ascus.
Thallus K−, KC−, C−, P−.
Habitat. In mountainous areas on siliceous rocks, especially granite.

A. pubescens x1

A. nigricans Forms dense tufted to decumbent mats up to 5cm high, the main branches up to 1.5mm diam. Usually matt pale pink or brown becoming darker towards the apices, becoming lighter in the herbarium (where it is inclined to stain the paper reddish-brown after a long period).  Distinct pseudocyphellae present, white, fusiform up to 0.8 mm long. Soralia and apothecia absent in Britain. This species may be recognised by the large pseudocyphellae, matt thallus, paler at the base and by the C+ reaction. The rare *Cornicularia* *divergens* is found in similar habitats and is also KC + red, C + rose-red but the thallus is a glossy not a matt brown. Thallus K + yellowish, KC + red (fades fast), C + rose red (fades fast), P + yellowish.

Habitat. Common locally in arctic-alpine heathland.

A. nigricans x1.5

A. ochroleuca Thallus erect up to 8cm, greenish-yellow fading to yellow. This is a very variable species but it may be distinguished from *A. sarmentosa* by being erect and terricolous. It differs from *A. nigricans* in its colour and the C− reaction of the cortex and the CK + deep yellow reaction of the medulla and from *A. sarmentosa* subsp. *vexillifera* by its habit, branching pattern and by the consistently KC−, and the CK + deep yellow reactions.

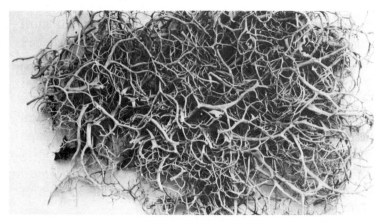

A. ochroleuca x1.5

Alectoria branching patterns x4 approx.

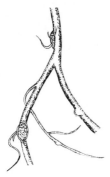

A. fuscescens

A. bicolor

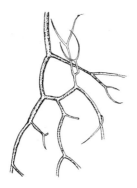

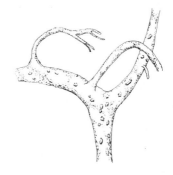

A. capillaris

A. sarmentosa

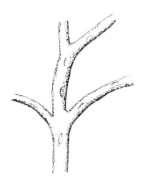

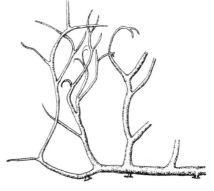

A. nigricans

A. pubescens **x8**

9

A. sarmentosa subsp. vexillifera Prostrate, up to 10cm long. Greenish-yellow when fresh. Main stems frequently very dorsiventrally flattened and foveolate up to 8mm wide. The base is inclined to die away leaving the thallus attached to the substrate by hapters. Pseudocyphellae abundant, white, fusiform about 1.0 x 0.2mm. Soralia absent.

Habitat. Decumbent on low vegetation between 300-1000 metres. Subsp. *sarmentosa;* the only British yellow pendent *Alectoria,* it occurs rarely on trees and rocks in the Scottish Highlands. The reactions of this and subsp. *vexillifera* are: cortexK− or + fy, KC + y, C—, P−: medulla KC + red or KC−, CK−.

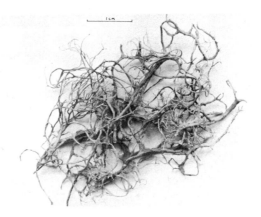

A. sarmentosa x1

ANAPTYCHIA Thallus fruticose or foliose. Apothecia lecanorine. Spores brown, 1 septate, 8 per ascus. Resembles *Physcia* from which it may be distinguished by the hyphae in the upper cortex which are parallel to the surface whilst in *Physcia* they are at right angles to the surface.

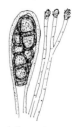

A. fusca x250

1. Thallus golden to dark brown adpressed to substrate........
....**A.fusca**

   Thallus grey to brownish not closely adpressed............2

2. Thallus K−..**A. ciliaris**
   Thallus K + y..3

3. Fairly erect and without apical soralia........**A. leucomelos**
   More or less prostrate and with apical soralia **A. obscurata**

Anaptychia fusca Thallus matt, golden to dark brown becoming dark brown-green when wet. Closely adpressed to the substrate, orbicular with long narrow imbricate lobes that widen towards the tips. Undersurface brown. Frequently fertile with discocarps up to 3mm or larger with contorted crenulate margins. K−, C bleaches thallus to pale yellow.

Habitat. Common on maritime rocks down to sea-level also rarely found inland on rocks, stone walls, and sometimes on trees in the west.

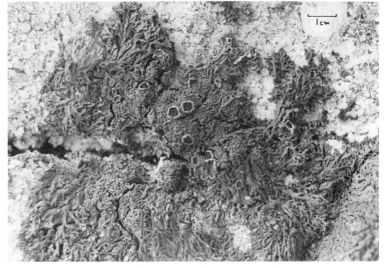

A. fusca ×1

11

A. ciliaris Thallus grey, tipped with brown and the surface often appearing furry. The thallus has long narrow lobes widening at the tips with long concolorous or dark marginal cilia, some of which attach it with discs to the substrate. The lower surface is concave and white with the hyphae forming a loose mat. Apothicia are common in unpolluted areas and are borne on short stalks, they have thick margins which become crenulate. The disc is black and frequently pruinose. K−, C−.

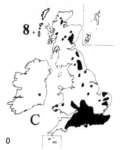

Habitat. Not rare on well-lit, wayside trees, more rarely on mossy rocks or moss.

A. ciliaris x3

Other British members of this genus [now in *Heteroderma*] are rare and include −

A. leucomelos Thallus whiter and finer than the preceding species. It has black cilia and also differs in being K + y. It has only been found sterile in Britain. Confined to S. and S.W. Britain.

A. obscurata Forms grey-white horizontal spreading rosettes and frequently has apical soralia K + y. Local in old woodland in the west.

ARTHONIA Crustose or with an immersed thallus. Apothecia rounded, or elongate to stellate more or less innate, immarginate with a rubbed down appearance, sometimes pruinose . Spores colourless or pale brown, fusiform 1-8 septate. Paraphyses branched and anastomosing. Name derived from the Greek "to sprinkle", referring to the scattered apothecia. The common British species are corticolous.

x1000

A. tumidula

1. Thallus grey-green to brown. Apothecia K− lirellate.......
    ....**A. radiata**
    Thallus contains yellow or orange, K + p or K + o 2
2. Apothecia orange-brown or red......................................3
    Apothecia purple-black or dark brown...........................4
3. Apothecia immarginate, orange to dark brown. On old trees..**A. didyma**
    Apothecia bright orange to scarlet often white pruinose. On smooth bark ....**A. tumidula**
4. Apothecia K + purple...**A. lurida**
    Apothecia K + orange...'.**A. spadicea**

Arthonia didyma Thallus creamy−yellow to dark-orange. Apothecia small, immarginate, convex, rounded, orange to dark − brown, irregular in shape. Spores usually 5 septate, clavate. Apothecia K + p. Habitat. Fairly common on shaded trees in old woodland sites.

A. didyma x10

A. tumidula (A. cinnabarina) Thallus light grey or frequently pale orange-brown with orange flecks, evanescent. Apothecia up to 0.5mm diam white pruinose or red, with bright orange margins, many of the apothecia growing in small groups. Spores 3-5 septate, clavate.

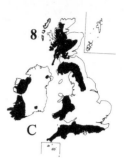

Orange areas and apothecia K + p.

Habitat. Common in shaded areas on smooth-barked trees.

A. tumidula x12

A. radiata Thallus grey-green to brown up to 3cm across. The junction between it and other lichens showing the black prothallus. Apothecia black and more or less stellate only slightly raised, sometimes flat and with less sharply defined apothecia (var. *swartziana*). Spores 3-septate, clavate.

K –.

Habitat. Very common on smooth-barked trees.

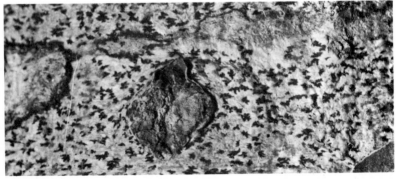

A. radiata x3

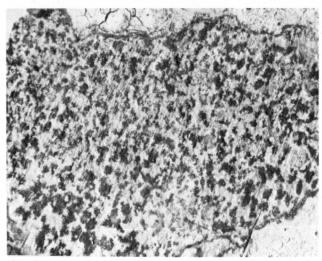

A. radiata var. *swartiana* x1.5

A. lurida Thallus orange evanescent. Apothecia purple – black. Spores 5 septate.
Apothecia K + p.
Habitat. Locally common on trees in sheltered western valleys.

5

A. spadicea Usually included in *A. lurida,* it has rounded, convex, shiny, dark-coloured apothecia that are K + o.
Habitat. Fairly common on trees in shaded situations.

A. spadicea x6

ARTHOPYRENIA Crustose, often immersed in the substrate. Perithecia black. Spores up to 8 per ascus. Spores colourless, ovate to fusiform and frequently clavate, 1-3 septate. Pseudoparaphyses frequently gelatinised.

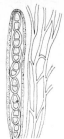

A. conoidea x250

1. Corticolous 2
   Saxicolous 5
2. Thallus white and cracked, mainly on rough bark 3
   Thallus thin and indeterminate, on smooth bark and twigs 4
3. Perithecia 0.5 − 1mm diam ....**A. gemmata**
   Perithecia 0.2 − 0.5mm diam ....**A. biformis**
4. Perithecia up to about 0.6mm diam ....**A. fallax**
   Perithecia up to about 0.3mm diam ....**A. punctiformis**
5. Perithecia about 0.25mm diam. On sea shells..**A. halodytes**
   Perithecia about 0.5mm diam, prominent 6
6. Perithecia up to 1mm diam, conical. Mainly hard limestone
   ....**A. conoidea**
   Perithecia up to 2mm, very prominent, hemispherical. On soft calcareous substrates ....**A. salweyi**

CORTICOLOUS

Arthopyrenia gemmata (A. alba) [Acrocordia gemmata] Thallus thin, white and cracked. Perithecia black, hemispherical, 0.5-1mm diam. Asci cylindrical. Spores uniserate, 8 per ascus. Spores colourless ellipsoid 20-30µm long.
Habitat. Common on rough bark of old trees.

A. gemmata x4

A. biformis Similar to the last species except that the perithecia are 0.2-0.5mm diam. Spores up to 15µm. Often found growing with *A. gemmata*.

A. fallax Thallus thin and indeterminate or evanescent. Perithecia piercing the epidermis of the host, looking as though varnished. Up to about 0.6mm diam. Habitat. Common on twigs and smooth bark in moderate shade.

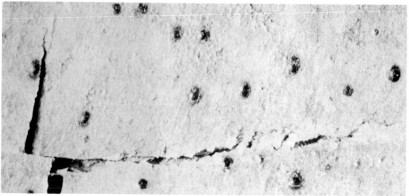

A. fallax x6

A. punctiformis Similar to the last species but with the thallus scarcely apparent to evanescent. The perithecia only about 0.3mm diam, with an oval shaped base and much smaller pycnidia.
Habitat. Common on smooth bark especially on young trees in moderate shade.

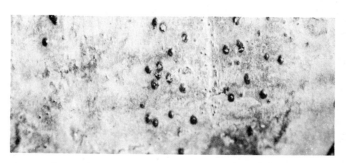

A. punctiformis x6

SAXICOLOUS

A. conoidea [Acrocordia conoidea] Thallus pink-grey thin or endolithic. Perithecia prominent, conical and large (up to 1mm). Ostioles not very apparent. Spores are arranged uniserately in the ascus. 1 septate, colourless.
Habitat. Frequent on hard limestones and other calcareous substrates.

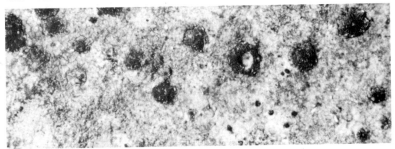

A. conoidea x6

A. salweyi [Acrocordia salweyi] Very similar to the above species but with larger perithecia up to almost 2mm, spherical and so prominent that they almost appear to be elevated.
Habitat. As *A. conoidea* but usually on softer rocks and more common in the S.E. on man-made substrates.

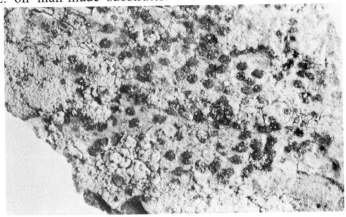

A. salwayi x6

A. halodytes Thallus brown and smooth on acid rocks but usually endolithic on calcareous substrates or shells. Perithecia are up to about 0.25mm and of various shapes, or immersed in pits when found on shells.
Habitat. Mainly around high water mark. Many limpets and barnacles around British shores have this species growing on them.

A. halodytes x3

BACIDIA Crustose. Discocarps lecideine and usually convex. Spores are colourless and only about 3μm wide, multiseptate but the septa are often indistinct. An apothecium should be sliced in half when examining specimens as the colour of the hypothecium is often important.

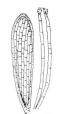

B. rubella x250

5. Apothecia about 0.3mm, cortex green when disturbed, spores in ascus spirally...................................**B. umbrina**
    Apothecia larger than 0.5mm diam.............................6

6. Apothecia up to 0.6mm contorted. Thallus bright green-grey.Found in or by water ....**B. inundata**
    Apothecia up to 1mm with distinct margins. Thallus yellow-green to grey ....**B. rubella**

7. Saxicolous..8
    On moss or soil..9

8. Apothecia about 0.3mm, convex. Thallus bright green-grey when disturbed. Spores spirally in ascus**B. umbrina**
    Apothecia up to about 0.6mm fairly flat. Thallus bright green-grey. In or by water..........................**B. inundata**

9. Thallus bright sulphur-yellow usually sterile..**B. citrinella**
    Thallus grey-green. Apothecia dark green to brown or black...10

10. Thallus thick, granulose, Acid heathland and peat. Apothecia dark green to black ....**B. lignaria**
    Thallus thin, slightly granulose. On moss. Apothecia greenish-brown to brown.........................**B. sabuletorum**

CORTICOLOUS

Bacidia endoleuca [B. laurocerasi] Thallus yellow-green to green-grey usually very granular. Apothecia almost black up to about 0.6mm diam. Hypothecium chestnut, K + violet or purple. Spores up to 85μm long and from 7–16 septate. Habitat. Fairly common mainly on conifers, when found on other trees it is usually the closely related *B. acerina*.

B. endoleuca x6

B. rubella Thallus yellow-green to grey, granular, or especially where sterile, the granules are pseudoisidiate. Apothecia orange-brown, not very convex with distinct margins in most fruits, up to or just over 1mm diam. Thecium about 70µm thick.

Habitat. Frequent mainly on elm but also *Acer* and other trees with nutrient-rich bark.

B. rubella x6

B. phacodes Thallus grey, granular or areolate, sometimes smooth. Apothecia flesh or pink in colour, slightly convex, scattered thickly over the surface and up to 1mm diam. The thecium is much thinner than in the last species being about 35–40µm in depth. Spores are about 35µm long and may be up to 15 septate but the septa are indistinct.

Habitat. Not common. Usually on nutrient-rich, rough-barked trees in damp and shade.

B. phacodes x6

B. chlorococca Thallus dirty green-grey, consisting of scurfy granules. Apothecia very small about 0.2mm diam and frequently immersed in the thallus. Discs convex light to dark brown and glossy. Spores 3–9 septate 20–40μm. Habitat. Fairly common on shaded trees, especially on twigs., Now thought to be very common in polluted regions in a sterile form.

B. chlorococca x8

SAXICOLOUS.

B. inundata Thallus bright green-grey which may dry to a straw colour. Thick with clumped granules, areolate or smooth. Apothecia small up to 0.6μm, light to dark brown, fairly flat or concave and contorted. Hypothecium fawn to brown. Spores up to 50μm 3–8 septate.

Habitat. Fairly common on wet rocks by or in streams and lakes, rarely found on trees.

B. inundata x8

B. umbrina Thallus loose granular grey-green mixed with a brighter green especially where the upper cortex is disturbed. Apothecia very small 0.3mm, convex, with a dark disc and a pale hypothecium. Spores 3 or more septate 20−45μm long and twisted together in the ascus.

Habitat. Common on rocks, walls or trees. One specimen was even found on weathered aluminium.

B. umbrina x8

ON MOSS OR SOIL

B. lignaria [Micarea lignaria] Thallus grey-green, verrucose. Apothecia convex, dark green to black with a colourless or light brown hypothecium and a blue-green epithecium. Spores 10−36um long, 3−10 septate.

Habitat. Common on peat or acid soil.

B. lignaria x6

B. citrinella [Arthrorhaphis citrinella]
Thallus of bright sulphur-yellow clumped granules, sometimes areolate. It has a brown prothallus. Usually sterile but when fertile it has many green to black apothecia growing in close groups. Discs plane or concave up to 0.6mm. Spores large up to 100μm.

Habitat. Hilly areas of Britain on soil or moss.

B. citrinella x6

B. sabuletorum Thallus light grey to almost black or greenish, more or less granulose. Ascocarps numerous, black, brownish when wet, immarginate, very convex and almost globose, hypothecium brown, spores 3–9 septate.

Habitat. Common on mosses on basic-barked trees, calcareous rocks and soil

B. sabuletorium x5

BAEOMYCES The generic name is derived from the Greek for a small mushroom. Primary thallus crustose or squamulose. Secondary thallus of short unbranched podetia lacking algal cells and looking more or less translucent. They bear capitate lecideine apothecia. Spores, colourless, simple or becoming 1

B. rufus x500

septate. 8 per ascus. The spores and some cells of the thallus contain oil globules.

Thallus grey, rather granular. Podetia up to 6mm high. Apothecia flesh-pink..**B. roseus**
Thallus green-grey, finely granular. Podetia up to 3mm high. Apothecia reddish-brown..............................**B. rufus**

Baeomyces roseus Thallus crustose, consisting of light grey to whitish granules of various sizes. Frequently sterile or with fairly smooth, simple podetia up to 6mm high bearing globular pale flesh-pink apothecia. Asci long and narrow containing 1 septate spores that often appear simple.
K + y–o, P + y.

4

Habitat. Common on peaty soil, usually in damp heathland. Frequently sterile in lowland areas.

B. roseus x10

B. rufus. Thallus greenish – grey, granulose or of minute squamules (particularly at the margins). The podetia differ from the last species in being somewhat darker in colour, furrowed, shorter and sessile or up to 3mm high. Apothecia flatter and reddish–brown in colour.

K + y.

Habitat. As the previous species but usually in more shaded, damp situations and not infrequently encountered on damp shaded siliceous rocks. Often found sterile.

B. rufus x10

BUELLIA Thallus placodioid or crustose, thin or areolate usually with a black prothallus. Apothecia black. Paraphyses simple with darker clavate apices. Spores brown, mainly 1 septate (becoming 3 septate to muriform in some species). Asci usually 8 spored. *B. aethalea* x500

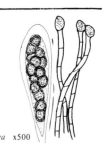

1. Thallus placodioid, pruinose sorediate ....**B. canescens**
   Thallus crustose, not placodioid 2

2. Corticolous...3
   Saxicolous 5

3. Thallus yellow-grey, thin, glossy, on smooth bark K + y
   ....**B. disciformis**
   Thallus not shining K⁻...4

4. Apothecia primrose with grey margins, spores appear muriform ....**B. alboatra** agg.
   Apothecia black, convex, thallus grey, warted or areolate
   ....**B. punctata**

5. On calcareous substrates. Spores appear muriform ....
....**B. alboatra** agg.
On siliceous rocks, apothecia immersed, at least when
young...6
6. Thallus grey with yellow-green soralia (rare)....**B. aspersa**
Thallus without soralia..7
7. Thallus warm grey, C + o ....**B. verruculosa**
Thallus C—..8
8. Thallus dark brown–grey K + o ....**B. aethalea**
Thallus light grey, P + o, K— or fy.............**B. stellulata**

Buellia canescens [Diploicia canescens]
This differs from the other species of
Buellia that follow in being strongly
placodioid. Thallus whitish to light grey,
darker in the centre. The lobes are
convex, long and narrow, wider at the
apices and very pruinose. The centre of
the thallus is usually covered in farinose

soralia. Except in the South ascocarps are rare. They have a
black disc and a thin black margin that becomes excluded.
Spores 1 septate.
K + y.
Habitat. Very common on basic and nutrient-enriched trees and
rocks, it becomes rare in Scotland.

B. canescens x2

B. punctata Thallus dark green-grey very variable from smooth to areolate. Usually fertile with many small, black, convex apothecia. The young fruits have indistinct margins. Spores ellipsoid, 1 septate, 8 per ascus.

K−.

Habitat. Common on trees, posts and occasionally on rocks.

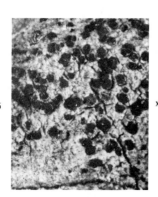

B. punctata x6

x4

B. disciformis Thallus thin, glossy, whitish to pale yellowish – grey sometimes a black prothallus is visible. Apothecia black up to 1mm diam., plane or concave with a thick margin. Spores simple to 3 septate.

K + y.

Habitat. Frequent mainly on smooth-barked trees.

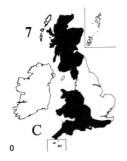

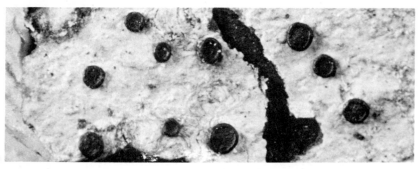

B. disciformis x10

B. alboatra agg. **[Diplotomma alboatrum]**
Thallus light grey. Thin and smooth to areolate, very variable. Apothecia with grey frequently crenulate margins and pruinose discs. Spores appear muriform. All reactions negative.
Habitat. Frequent on basic bark and nutrient – enriched trees and hard calcareous rocks and mortar.

B. alboatra x6

B. aethalea Thallus dark grey to brown-grey, areolate in the centre, less so near the darker margin which is visible between the areolae. Apothecia immersed, small with a black disc and found on the older parts of the thallus. Spores 1 septate.
K + o.
Habitat. Frequent on well-lit siliceous rocks.

B. aethalea x15

B. stellulata Thallus light grey, areolate on a broad radiating dark prothallus. Apothecia immersed when young but becoming more prominent. Discs black. Spores 1 septate, 8–14µm long, slightly constricted at the septum.
P + y.
Habitat. Common on well-lit siliceous rocks, mainly in maritime areas.

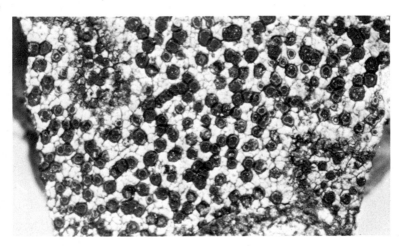

B. stellulata x6

B. verruculosa Thallus warm greenish-grey or yellowish-grey, areolate with a distinct black prothallus. Apothecia immersed when young usually only one in each areola. Discs black with an irregular crenulate margin. Spores 1 septate 11–20µm long.
C + O.

Habitat. Not common. Found on smooth well-lit siliceous rocks, flints and shingle mainly in the south-east.
B. aspersa is a rare species found in similar habitats in the south-east but has minute light yellowish-green soralia which are C + or − orange.

B. verruculosa x10

CALICIACEAE The genera contained in this family have a thin crustose thallus. The apothecia are borne on the end of short stalks of up to about 2mm high. The asci break down to a loose spore mass (a mazaedium). Genera with very short stalks described in this book may be separated as follows:

Simple spores
Spores colourless ....**Coniocybe**
Spores brown...**Chaenotheca**
Spores septate, brown or becoming brown
1 Septate...**Calicium**
3 Septate (may be 1 septate when young)...........**Stenocybe**

CALICIUM The name is probably derived from calix 'a wine-cup'. Thallus thin or granular. Apothecia are on stalks like small pins. The asci disintegrates to leave a powdery black spore mass (mazaedium). Spores 1 septate, brown.

C. abietinum x1000

31

1. Thallus thick, green, granulose ....**C. viride**
   Thallus thin, or almost absent, greyish 2
2. Capitulum black or pale grey, open...........................3
   Capitulum light to dark brown, pruinose almost globose
   ....**C. salicinum**
3. Spore mass at least slightly pruinose, exciple white........
   ....**C. glaucellum**
   Spore mass not pruinose, exciple not white.**C. abietinum**

C. abietinum   *C. glaucellum*   *C. salicinum*   *C. viride*

Calicium glaucellum Thallus thin, light grey often immersed and sometimes scarcely apparent. Apothecia are often crowded over the thallus and are borne on short, stout, black stalks up to 0.5mm high. Apothecia are pruinose with a white exciple.

Habitat. Common on decorticated wood and old trees particularly conifers.

C. glaucellum x20

C. abietinum Very similar to the previous species but differs in the apothecia which are not pruinose and do not have a white exciple.
Habitat. Uncommon. Found in similar habitats to *C. glaucellum.*

C salicinum Thallus pale grey with a bluish tinge, sometimes scarcely apparent. Apothecia are light brown on darker brown to black stalks 0.4 − 1.5mm high. Not pruinose.
Habitat.Frequent on decorticated wood and old bark, mainly in the south.

C. salicinum x20

C. viride Thallus bright emerald-green to sulphurous yellow-green becoming browner when dry, granulose. The thallus is usually thicker than in the previous two species. Frequently sterile. Apothecia black, naked on stalks 1-2mm high. Cups with a reddish-brown pruina.
Habitat. Common on the dry bark of trees, particularly oak and conifers.

C. viride x12

CALOPLACA Thallus more or less placodioid (sect. *Gasparrinia*) or crustose. Many species have a yellow or orange thallus, or at least the apothecia are orange or red, containing parietin which produces a K + purple reaction. Soredia and isidia are present in some species. Apothecia are lecanorine or

C. saxicola x500

lecideine. Spores colourless, polarilocular, and spore shape is useful in identification. Spores 8 per ascus in species described.

Caloplaca spore shapes

Type 1, showing variations in septum thickness

Type 2    Type 3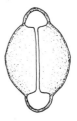

 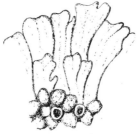 

C. saxicola	*C. aurantia*	*C. heppiana*
Yellow to yellow-brown	golden creamy-yellow	Bright orange
Lobes convex	Lobes flat	Lobes convex
short and palmate	very palmate	slightly palmate
often pruinose	not pruinose	usually pruinose

1. Thallus grey or white. K −. Apothecia may be K + crimson 2

   Thallus yellow or orange. K + crimson 6

2. Discs rust-red 3

   Discs yellow to deep orange...4

3. Apothecia becoming translucent and greener when wet .... **C. caesiorufa**

   Apothecia unchanged on wetting ....**C. ferruginea**

4. Thallus white. Apothecia up to 0.5mm, yellow–orange ....**C. lactea**

   Thallus grey, or white and placodioid. Apothecia larger than 0.5mm or absent..5

5 a. Apothecia up to 0.75mm often crowded. Bright orange with concolorous margins.............................**C. luteoalba**

   b. Apothecia up to 2mm usually scattered, orange-yellow with a grey margin...**C. cerina**

   c. Thallus scurfy or sorediate, slightly placodioid**C. teicholyta**

6. Thallus granular or thin, not lobate.............................7

   Thallus lobate, at least at the margins........................10

7. Thallus yellow-brown to golden; thin, / or orange and granular...8

   Thallus lime–yellow to greenish–yellow, granular, sorediate ....**C. citrina**

8. Thallus orange, granular, maritime ....**C. marina**

   Thallus yellow-brown to greenish-yellow, thin or endolithic 9

9. Spores with 2 cells.....................................**C. ochracea**

   Spores with 4 cells ....**C. tetrasticha**

10. Thallus with isidia or soralia......................................11

    Thallus lacking isidia or soralia, usually fertile...........14

11. Thallus isidiate 12

    Thallus sorediate...13

12. Isidia dense and coralloid, a crust with only poorly defined lobes...**C. littorea**

    Isidia scattered and coarse, lobate.............**C. verruculifera**

13. Lobes short and close. Soralia concolorous with thallus open habitats ....**C. decipiens**

    Lobes long, narrow and spaced out. Soralia yellow. Thallus orange, shaded rocks...................................**C. cirrochroa**

14. Thallus yellow to creamy orange. Lobes very flattened ....**C. aurantia**

Thallus yellow to deep orange, lobes obscure and/or convex...15

15. Lobes obscure. Thallus mainly yellow, pruinose irregular granules. Found on South-facing church walls in the East ....**C. ruderum**

Thallus lobate and/or orange.....................................16

16. Thallus yellow-brown, more brown in centre, often pruinose .... **C. saxicola (C. murorum)**

Thallus orange..17

17. Thallus with long narrow lobes, pruinose......**C. heppiana**

Strictly maritime at H.W.M., or orange zone not pruinose 18

18. Forming a regular rosettes, lobes long, extending from near the centre of the thallus.............................**C. thallincola**

Forming diffuse patches. Lobes irregular or scattered lobules, at about H.W.M................................**C. marina**

THALLUS GREY OR WHITE, CRUSTOSE.
Cortex K− (apothecia may be K + crimson)

Caloplaca cerina Thallus light grey, thin to almost areolate, sometimes with a black prothallus. Apothecia large (up to 2mm diam), crowded, with a bright orange-yellow roughened disc and a thick grey margin. Spores type 1.
Discs K + crimson.
Habitat. Common on basic and nutrient-rich bark of deciduous trees of unpolluted areas,becoming rarer. The var.*chlorina* has an areolate dark grey-green thallus, smaller apothecia (1mm) and is found on shaded rocks in damp areas.

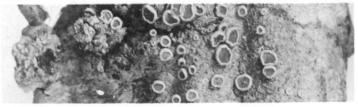

C. cerina x5

C. caesiorufa Thallus dark grey, granular or areolate. Apothecia chestnut to rust-brown when dry, with a much paler orange margin. Disc plane, becoming convex. Spores type 3 or slightly curved. Differs from *C. ferruginea* in the darker discocarps which becomes greener on wetting and also by the paler margins.

Habitat. Common on siliceous maritime rocks.

C. ferruginea Similar to the last species but may have a lighter or evanescent thallus. Apothecia about 1mm diam. rust red, plane becoming convex. Colour does not change with wetting and the margins are only slightly paler. Spores Type 1.

Apothecia K + crimson.

Habitat. Common on siliceous rocks, inland as well as maritime, occasionally on trees. Mainly in the west and north of Britain. *C. holocarpa* also has rust-red apothecia but these become very convex when mature and it is found on more calcareous substrates.

C. ferruginea x6

C. lactea Thallus white, thin or endolithic. Apothecia to 0.5mm diam plane or concave when young. Disc orange-yellow with a margin which becomes obscured ' as the apothecium becomes mature and convex. Spores type 1 with a thin septum.
Apothecia K + crimson.
Habitat. Rare, on calcareous rocks (occasionally on trees).

C. lactea x7

C. luteoalba Thallus grey, thin or evanescent, Apothecia frequent and crowded. Innate when young becoming convex, up to 0.75mm, bright orange with a concolorous margin. Spores Type 1 with a thin septum.
Apothecia K + crimson.
Habitat. Not uncommon on elm, to which it is largely confined. It has now become rare due to the loss of elms from disease. It is also found on calcareous rocks where it may be endolithic.

C. luteoalba x6

THALLUS YELLOW OR ORANGE, NOT LOBATE.
K + crimson.

C. citrina Thallus lime – yellow to greenish-yellow. Frequently sterile and sorediate. Apothecia yellow-orange often having yellow granules and a thick paler margin. Spore type 1 (septum 1/3 length of spore).
Habitat. Common on calcareous substrates and occasionally on nutrient-rich bark on trees. It may be separated from *Candelariella* sp. by the K + crimson reaction.

C. citrina x6

C. ochracea Thallus light yellow-brown to pale golden-yellow, superficial, almost granular, felted, thin, continuous. Apothecia up to 0.4mm dark orange-yellow with a thick paler margin. Spores type 1 with a thick septum.
Habitat. Common on maritime and inland hard calcareous substrates. The very similar and doubtfully distinct *C. tetrasticha* differs in having 4 celled spores of type 2.

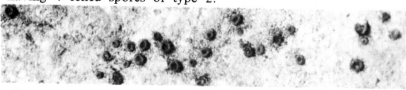

C. ochracea x8

THALLUS AND APOTHECIA YELLOW, LOBATE.
K + crimson
Without isidia or soralia, usually fertile

C. aurantia Thallus pale egg to golden yellow, sometimes blackened in the centre. Lobes adpressed, long, distinctly flat, palmate and usually matt. The centre of the thallus is areolate and may obscure much of the placodioid margin. Apothecia flat to slightly convex, disc orange-brown with a slightly lighter margin. Spores type 3.

Habitat. Common on hard calcareous rocks and tombstones .

C. aurantia x0.8

C. heppiana Thallus orange. Lobes narrow, convex, wider at the apices which may be pruinose and crenulate. The centre of the thallus may be almost lobate. Apothecia numerous, orange with paler margins, flat or only slightly convex. Spores type 3.

Habitat. Very common on hard calcareous rocks and tombstones, more rarely on brick.

C. heppiana x3

40

C. saxicola (C. murorum) Thallus yellow to brownish – yellow. Lobes narrow, convex, fairly short, usually very pruinose. The centre of the thallus is lobular, granulose and darker than the lobes. Apothecia dark orange with paler margins. Spores Type 1, 9-16 × 4.5-7 µm. The thallus is very variable and

may be reduced to separate lobules. It may be separated with certainty from the two preceding species by the spore shape. K + crimson.

Habitat. Common on hard calcareous rocks and tombstones, very rarely on siliceous rocks. Particularly common in the south and west.

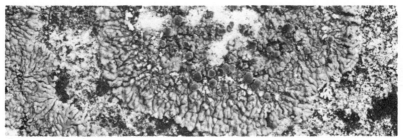

C. saxicola x3

C. ruderum Superficially resembles *C. citrina* but has a yellow very pruinose thallus of convex irregular granules. The apothecia have thick margins and the disc is never convex. K + crimson.

Habitat. Locally frequent but may be overlooked. Found in eastern England on well-lit, soft calcareous substrates especially the south-facing walls of churches.

C. ruderum x6

C. teicholyta Thallus white to blueish-grey, scurfy, becoming sorediate in the centre. It is often slightly placodioid. Usually infertile but when in fruit it has orange apothecia.

Spores Type 1, 11-18 × 8-10μm.

Cortex K−. Apothecia K + crimson.

Habitat. Common in the south-east, mainly on calcareous substrates, especially tombstones. Rare in the rest of Britain.

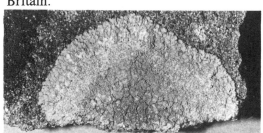

C. teicholyta x3

Thallus isidiate

C. verruculifera (C. granulosa) Thallus yellow-orange, pruinose. Lobes long, narrow, very convex branched with wider tips. Centre of the thallus areolate with irregular, granular isidia extending on to the inner ends of the lobes. Apothecia rare, flat, yellow-orange. Spores Type 1, 10-16 × 5-8 μm.

K + crimson.

Habitat. Not uncommon locally on hard siliceous rocks just above high-water mark.

C. verruculifera x7

C. littorea Thallus deep orange-yellow, indistinctly lobed. The thallus is essentially aerolate but largely concealed by dense masses of orange globular to coralloid isidia. Apothecia very rare, flat, orange-yellow and pruinose. Spores Type 1, 11-14 × 5-7 µm. K + crimson.

Habitat. A local south-western Mediteranean species of hard, siliceous, maritime rocks, well above high-water mark.

C. littorea x4

CANDELARIA Thallus minutely foliose. Apothecia lecanorine. Spores colourless, simple, 8 + per ascus. This genus is represented in Britain by only one species.

C. concolor x350

Candelaria concolor Thallus greenish-yellow to lemon–yellow consisting of dense tufts of erect minute (to 1mm) lobules with incised ends which are sorediate on the margin. Undersurface white with rhizinae. Apothecia fairly rare, dirty yellow with a roughened margin. May be distinguished from *Xanthoria candelaria* by its K− reaction.

45

Habitat. A local and decreasing species now found in areas of low pollution. Found on well-lit to lightly shaded nutrient-rich bark of trees, also on fences and exceptionally on rocks.

C. concolor x6   *C. concolor x12*

CANDELARIELLA Thallus crustose or subsquamulose to placodioid. Apothecia lecanorine. Spores simple, colourless, normally 8, but may be up to 32 per ascus. Distinguished from *Caloplaca* species by the consistently K− reaction.

C. vitellina x350

1. Thallus placodioid, pruinose ....**C. medians**
    Thallus crustose, granular..2
2. Thallus, scattered granules. Spores 8 per ascus...**C. aurella**
    Thallus irregular, conspicuous clumped granules. Spores more than 8 per ascus....................................**C. vitellina**

Candelariella medians Thallus yellow. Lobes flattened and pruinose, the centre areolate. Apothecia rare, brown-yellow. May be distinguished from *Caloplaca* species by the K− reaction and especially from *Caloplaca heppiana* by its lighter, more yellow colour.

Habitat. Formerly a very rare species of hard calcareous rocks but now common on man-made calcareous substrates, eg., concrete, asbestos-cement, tombstones.

C. medians x2

C. aurella Thallus mustard yellow, consisting of thinly scattered granules on a distinctive black prothallus. Apothecia almost always present. Less than 1mm diam with a dirty yellow-brown disc. The margins become crenulate. Spores 8 per ascus.

K− This reaction separates this and the following species from the similar *Caloplaca citrina.*

Habitat. Common on nutrient-enriched calcareous rocks, bricks and mortar. Commonest in the south and east.

C. aurella x10

C. vitellina Thallus mustard – yellow, consisting of larger, flatter granules than the previous species. The granules are irregular in shape and often clump together to form a thick, frequently areolate, crust several centimetres across. Apothecia common up to 1mm diam, dirty yellow. Spores more than 8 per ascus.

Habitat. Common on nutrient – enriched siliceous rocks especially those used by birds. More rarely on slightly calcareous rocks, bricks and trees. More common than *C. aurella* except in fairly heavily polluted areas.

C. vitellina x12

CATILLARIA Thallus crustose. Apothecia lecideine. Spores colourless, 1(–3) septate, 8 per ascus.

This genus contains the only British species that grows directly on leaves. This is the very rare *C. bouteillei* that is found mainly on well-lit box leaves in south-east England.

C. lenticularis x600

1. Corticolous 2
   Saxicolous...7
2. K + y or faint yellow, without apothecia 3
   K + or − with apothecia...4
3. Thallus light grey with numerous black, dust-like pycnidia, 0.2mm diam ....**C. griffithii**
   Thallus bright grey-green, granulose, often sorediate, usually orbicular ....**C. lightfootii**

4. Thallus grey-green to green...5
    Thallus light grey to black..6
5. Apothecia globose flesh pink to brown, damp shade in the
    west... **C. sphaeroides**
    Apothecia dark brown. Thallus granulose, sorediate. In
    circular patches ....**C. lightfootii**
6. Thallus light grey. Apothecia light to dark brown...........
    ....**C. griffithii**
    Thallus grey to black often evanescent. Apothecia small,
    black..**C. chalybeia**
7. Thallus grey to black or endolithic. Apothecia very small,
    dark red to black, calc. rock.......................**C. lenticularis**
    Thallus grey to black, smooth or warted or endolithic.
    Apothecia small, black, silic. rock ....**C. chalybeia**

CORTICOLOUS

Catillaria griffithii Thallus light grey to
almost whitish, shining or warted.
Mainly found without apothecia but
then easily recognised by the numerous
small dust-like pycnidia about 0.2mm
diam. Apothecia flesh coloured to light
brown, with a slightly lighter thin
margin, becoming darker with age, often
convex and distorted. Spores 1 septate.
K + y, C−.

Habitat. One of the more common corticolous species,
on all but the more acid bark or wood.

C. griffithii x7

C. lightfootii [Fuscidea lightfootii] Thallus bright grey-green, often distinctly granulose, usually sorediate, thick, sharply defined, and in neat circular patches. Often found infertile. Apothecia up to 1mm diam very dark brown to almost black, flat to slightly convex, a

slightly paler thin margin is usually present. Spores 1 septate, constricted in the centre, with obtuse ends. K− or + , C−.

May be confused with *Lecidella elaeochroma,* but it is C− (*L. elaeochroma* may be C− in polluted areas), has 1 septate (sometimes indistinct) constricted spores, and a more granular thallus.

Habitat. Frequent on smooth bark, particularly on twigs. Found in damp areas in the south and west.

C. lightfootii x2.5

C. sphaeroides Thallus dark green-grey to green, granular, almost felted. Apothecia light brown to flesh−pink, prominent, almost globose and becoming contorted. Spores 1 septate, simple when young. K−, C−.

Habitat. A rather local species of old deciduous woodlands, mainly found on very shaded mossy trees, often by streams, sometimes on soil.

C. sphaeroides x5

SAXICOLOUS

C. chalybeia Thallus grey to black effuse, sometimes evanescent, or areolate. Apothecia small about 0.5mm, black, convex or flat with a thin margin. Paraphyses with black tips. Spores 1 septate.
K−, C−.
Habitat. Common on hard siliceous rocks and walls, particularly near the sea, rarely also on trees.

C. lenticularis Similar to the last species but the thallus may be almost entirely endolithic. It may be separated by the very small dark red apothecia with more prominent margins and the dark brown tips of the clavate paraphyses.
Habitat. Common on calcareous rocks but easily overlooked. Rarer in Scotland.

C. lenticularis x3

CAVERNULARIA Thallus foliose with deep depressions on the lower surface. Apothecia lecanorine, spores colourless 8 per ascus. There is only one British species.

Cavernularia hultenii Thallus grey, orbicular up to 2cm in diam. Lobes rarely more than 1mm wide with pale-coloured soralia on the apices. Resembles a small *Hypogymnia pysodes* but the thallus is not completely hollow and the dark brown undersurface has numerous distinctive dark pits.

9

0

Apothecia not found in Britain, brown on short stalks Spores very small and globose.

Cortex K + , Medulla KC + , C−, P−.

Habitat. A rare species of pine, birch and rowan trees and heather stems in old pine forests of central and north-western Scotland.

C. hultenii x3

CETRARIA Thallus foliose to almost fruticose. Rhizinae absent or sparse and confined to the central region. Apothecia rare in Britain, usually on the margins. Spores colourless, simple, usually 8 per ascus. A mainly Northern genus that is poorly represented in Britain.

The name is derived from the Greek 'cetra' from the shield-shaped apothecia.

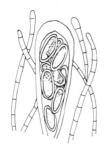

C. islandica x600

Thallus greenish-brown, tufted. K− ....**C. chlorophylla**
Thallus grey-green, fairly erect. K + y.........**Platismatia glauca**
Thallus creamy-yellow. High altitudes in Scotland. KC + y ..
....**C. nivalis**
Thallus chestnut to brown. P + red ....**C. islandica**

Cetraria chlorophylla Thallus dark green to brown (dull green when wet), lobes erect, rarely rising above 1cm from the substrate and forming tufts, apices of lobes incised, with dark soralia on the margin. Undersurface pale coffee-brown, shiny and wrinkled, paler towards the centre where there are a few simple rhizinae.

It may be separated from the rather similar *Platismatia glauca* (K + y) by the negative reaction, its greenish-brown colour as opposed to grey-green (not much greener when wet) of *P. glauca* and its smaller size.

Habitat. Common in upland areas particularly on coniferous trees, fence posts, and siliceous rocks. It is often found in the south and Midlands on both coniferous and deciduous trees.

C. chlorophylla x1

C. nivalis Thallus creamy-yellow, both surfaces more yellow towards the base. Forming loose tufts up to 5cm high. The lobes are long and narrow, deeply incised and undulate.

KC + y.

Habitat. Locally abundant in ericaceous heaths at high altitudes in the Scottish Highlands, just below the line of the longest persisting winter snow.

53

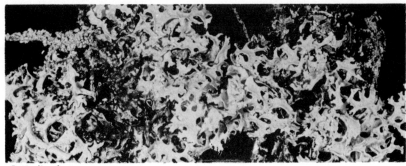
C. nivalis x3

C. islandica Thallus strap-like, shining, chestnut to dark brown on both sides, frequently more red towards the base, forming dense tufts or straggling entangled mats up to about 8cm high loosely attached to the substrate. Lobes long, thin, curled inwards and deeply incised, ciliate on the margins. The upper and lower surfaces have scattered, white, rather fusiform pseudocyphellae.

Med. P + intensely red throughout (in Britain).

Habitat. Common on ericaceous heaths in the Scottish Highlands becoming much less common in England and Ireland. Still known from single sites on heaths in Derbyshire, Lincolnshire and Norfolk.

This is "Iceland Moss" which due to the high isolichenin content, was once soaked for a few days to remove the bitter acids it contains, then boiled and eaten either as a broth or jelly. It also forms an important food for reindeer and caribou.

C. islandica x125

CHAENOTHECA Thallus crustose and granular. Apothecia yellow to dark brown on dark stalks, so as to resemble pins. Asci and paraphyses breaking down to form a powdery mass at maturity. Distinguished from other genera with stalked apothecia by the simple, spherical, brown spores.

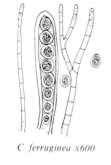

C. ferruginea x600

Chaenotheca ferruginea Thallus blue-grey to orange-grey with orange or mustard-yellow patches, it often forms an areolate crust. Often found infertile but apothecia are common, dark brown, convex with a paler yellow-orange or brown spore mass. Apothecial stalks about 1-2mm tall but may be rudimentary in some specimens.

Thallus K−, orange patches K + red.

Habitat. Frequent in bark recesses of deciduous trees or old pines (it avoids direct rain or water run off), particularly in the north and east. Common in areas of moderate air pollution but rarer in the west.

C. ferruginea x15

CLADONIA The generic name is derived from the Greek for "a twig". Primary thallus crustose or squamulose, disappearing or persistent. Secondary thallus fruticose, consisting of hollow podetia bearing apothecia at their tips. Apothecia lecideine. Spores normally simple, colourless, 8 per ascus.

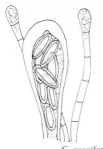

C. coccifera x600

Some of the larger species form an important fodder source for reindeer and caribou in subarctic and northern boreal areas. It takes from 4 to as many as 30 years for a pasture to regenerate for re-cropping. They have been used in Scandinavia for producing antibiotics and even alcohol in the U.S.S.R. The more bush-like species are dyed and used as trees in model railways, etc.

1. Apothecia red (K + crimson)...2
   Apothecia brown (K −) or absent.....................................8
2. Podetia grey, K −...**C. floerkeana**
   Podetia yellow-grey to green, or if grey K + y..............3
3. Podetia K + y or r, P + o or r.......................................4
   Podetia K −, KC + y, P −...6
4. Primary squamules very farinose sorediate on undersurface K + deep yellow ....**C. digitata**
   Primary squamules not sorediate on undersurface K + yellow...5
5. Podetia unbranched, without a distinct cup...**C. macilenta**
   Podetia often branched, hornlike and usually proliferating from the rim of a deformed cup ....**C. polydactyla**
6. Podetia very narrow, never sorediate, upland species...**C. bellidiflora**
   Podetia widening to a cup, sorediate, sometimes also squamulose, upland or not...7
7. Primary thallus persistent, podetia stout, cup flared, common on sand and peat ....**C. coccifera**
   Primary thallus decays early, podetia slender and expanding from the base, not abruptly flared....................**C. gonecha**
8. Primary thallus granular. Podetia papillate often in a dense mass ....**Pycnothelia papillaria**

Primary thallus squamulose or not, podetia prominent .9
9a. Thallus an interwoven, often much branched mat of tubular podetia 10
b. Thallus predominantly of primary squamules 19
c. Thallus predominantly of podetia which are not interwoven and often sparsely, or not branched 24
10. K + yellow 11
    K – 13
11. Thallus light grey with a distinctive brownish-mauve tinge; many apical branches all bent in one direction, P + red .... **C. rangiferina**
    Apical branches not all bent in one direction, usually more calcareous substrates 12
12. Thallus brown-grey, podetia prostrate, contorted, not with squamules .... **C. furcata** sub sp. **subrangiformis**
    Thallus grey-green, podetia not contorted; forming a more or less erect mat; often with some squamules **C. rangiformis**
13. P – 14
    P + ... 16
14. Thallus sparsely branched, yellowish or brown-grey to olive green 15
    Thallus richly branched, pale grey .... **C. impexa**
15. Thallus yellow to yellowish–brown, little or not branched .... **C. uncialis**
    Thallus brown-grey to olive-green, no yellow tinge, contorted, more or less erect, forming lax tufts .... **C. rangiformis**
16. Thallus ashy–grey to green-grey, richly (dichotomously) branched .... **C. tenuis**
    Thallus green-grey or brown-grey, side branches more widely spaced 17
17. Branches strongly curved in one direction, tri-, tetrachotomously branched .... **C. arbuscula**
    Branches not strongly curved in one direction 18
18. Branches diverging at a narrow angle, brown-green, mainly acid substrates. Common and variable .... **C. furcata**
    Branches diverging at a wider angle, grey-green to pale brown-green, mainly on dunes and calcareous substrates .... **C. rangiformis**

19. C + bright green (acid heathland)......................**C. strepsilis**
    C −..20
20. Undersurface of squamules, yellowish.............**C. foliacea**
    Undersurface of squamules, white................................21
21. Squamules K + yellow..22
    Squamules K −..23
22. Squamules blue-green, densely tufted, up to 5mm wide, blackened at base, mainly acid rocks......**C. subcervicornis**
    Squamules grey-green, less than 2mm wide, not blackened at base, mainly on peat and tree bases.........**C. macilenta**
23. Squamules waxy blue-green, up to 5mm wide, often tufted, undersurface pruinose....................................**C. cervicornis**
    Squamules bright green, up to 3mm wide, usually spreading, undersurface not pruinose............**C. coniocraea**
24. Podetia longitudinally split open, with fringed cups
    ....**C. crispata**
    Podetia not split open longitudinally............................25
25. Podetia not terminating in a wide cup........................26
    Podetia terminating in a wide cup................................30
26. Podetia delicate, branched with minute brownish-grey incised squamules, K + y....................................**C. parasitica**
    Podetia usually robust, squamules conspicuous, not branched, K + yellow or K −..27
27. Podetia with green squamules, K + yellow to orange
    ....**C. squamosa** var. **allosquamosa**
    Podetia K −..28
28. Podetia more or less densely green or brown-green squamulose throughout, not farinose sorediate
    ....**C. squamosa**
    Podetia slightly squamulose towards base, sorediate or corticate above..29
29. Upper part sorediate sometimes with a very narrow cup (shorter)..**C. coniocraea**
    Upper part decorticate with a narrow cup (taller)
    ....**C. ochrochlora**
30. Podetia branched or having secondary podetia growing from them..31
    Podetia simple, regular (apothecia sometimes on short stalks around rim of cup)..32

31. Secondary podetia growing from the centre of primary podetia, K − ....**C. verticillata**
Secondary podetia growing from the rim of the primary podetia, K + yellow ....**C. squamosa** var. **squamosa**

32. Podetia finely sorediate, expanding abruptly "golf tee" shaped ....**C. fimbriata**
Podetia coarsely sorediate or squamulose-warted, gradually expanding from the base...33

33. Podetia and cup-interior sorediate ....**C. chlorophaea**
Podetia and cup warted or squamulose, not sorediate ....**C. pyxidata**

| Dichotomous | Trichotomous | Tetrachotomous |

Cladonia branching patterns

APOTHECIA BROWN
PRIMARY THALLUS ABSENT OR INSIGNIFICANT.
Podetia branched. Only loosely or not attached to the substrate.
SECONDARY THALLUS BROWN-GREY GREEN-GREY

Cladonia arbuscula Primary thallus granular, evanescent. Podetia forming tufted mats up to 6cm high, green-grey almost always with a yellowish tinge when fresh. Branching di- or trichotomous, the top branches being strongly recurved mainly in one direction. The surface of the podetia is

light and covered with darker patches. The axils are open. KC + yellow, P + red. The very rare *C. mitis* is P− and the branches are less strongly orientated in one direction.
Habitat. Common on acid heathlands, particularly peat moors in upland areas, also found on dunes.

C. arbuscula x0.5

C. crispata var. **cetrariiformis** Primary thallus of squamules up to 3mm long, sometimes persisting. Podetia to about 5cm high, brown-grey to olive-green, reticulated especially in the paler specimens, axils widely open, podetia squamulose. Sometimes bears sharply flaring cups which are open into the

interior of the poditium. The margins bearing other cups which in turn have digitate margins.

Reactions negative.

Habitat. Common on acid heathlands and peat bogs, also on decaying trees. Most common in the north and west but one of the richest sites in Britain is in Norfolk.

C. crispata x1.5

C. furcata A very variable species. The podetia forming a loose mat. Brown-grey to olive-green, sometimes with a purplish tinge. Surface of the podetia almost smooth except for slight lighter coloured indentations. Branches dichotomously at wide angles with the axils normally closed. Usually infertile.

Apothecia small, brown, globose on the tips of the branches. Usually K−, P + red.

Habitat. Common on acid heathlands and in woods on soil throughout the British Isles. The coarse and contorted, K + yellow, subspecies *subrangiformis* occurs in calcareous grassland.

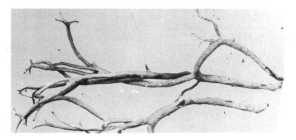

C. furcata x2.5

C. rangiformis Superficially similar to *C. furcata* but usually lighter in colour due to the larger areas of indentations and branching at a wider angle.

Usually K + yellow, P + red but the reactions vary.

Habitat. Common on similar habitats to *C. furcata* but appears to prefer more basic soils, calcareous grassland and stabilised dunes.

C

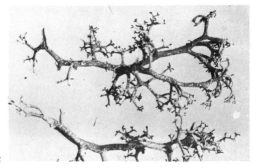

C. rangiformis x2.5

C. tenuis var. **leucophaea [C. ciliata]**
Podetia green-grey with a purplish tinge.
Smaller and more richly branched with
shorter lateral branches than either of
the two preceding species. It is a more
delicate blue than either *C. arbuscula* or
C. impexa with which it is most
frequently confused. It is mainly

dichotomously branched, branch tips not curled down.
K–, KC–, P + red. The rare var. *tenuis* has a yellowish to light
grey thallus and is KC + yellow.
Habitat. Common on dunes and peat moors.

C. tenuis x2

THALLUS YELLOW-GREEN

C. uncialis subsp. **biuncialis** Thallus
swollen, normally stouter, yellower and
less branched than the preceding species
(up to about 3mm diam). Sparsely and
strictly dichotomously branched and
widening at the open axils. Forms loose
mats or may be scattered over the
substrate.
KC + yellowish, P–.

Habitat. Common on acid heathlands especially peat bogs even
in waterlogged areas where maritime types can occur (only
subsp. *biuncialis* occurs in the British Isles).

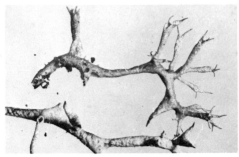

C. uncialis x2

THALLUS WHITE OR GREY
(The preceding species may bleach to a light colour)

C. impexa [C. portentosa] Thallus light grey or pale cream very richly branched, branching mainly trichotomous but the final division is usually dichotomous. The branchlets spreading out in all directions. It forms compact delicate tufted interwoven mats up 3cm high. K−, KC + y, P− (Both *C. tenuis* and *C. arbuscula* are P + red).

Habitat. Common on heaths, dunes and peat moors.

C. impexa x4.5

C. rangiferina Thallus light grey with a purple tinge. Richly branched but at a smaller angle than *C. impexa*. Branching usually dichotomous but may be tetrachotomous. Main branches often all curved in the same direction. Forms extensive, interwoven mats up to 5cm tall.

P + red, K + y. The K + y reaction purple tinge, and its usually coarser form separate it from *C. impexa* and *C. arbuscula*. Habitat. Common on Scottish mountains but not essentially an arctic species and it can be found on other heathlands.

C. rangiferina x1.5

PRIMARY THALLUS,
PERSISTENT AND DOMINANT
(Podetia if present less than twice the length of a squamule and growing on a squamule)

C. cervicornis [C. verticillata] Primary thallus up to 2cm high but usually less. Squamules fairly deeply incised. Upper surface blue-green to green. Undersurface pruinose, not blackened towards the base (see *C. subcervicornis*). Podetia not very distorted, with other podetia often arising from the centre of  the cups. Now considered to be synonymous with *C. verticillata*.

P + red, K−.

Habitat. Common on acid heathlands, stabilised shingle, rocks, etc.

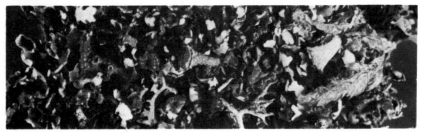

C. cervicornis x4

C. subcervicornis Primary thallus up to 2cm high, bluntly incised at the tip. Upper surface blue-green to apple-green. Undersurface, white, pruinose and blackened towards the base. Forms compact, dense, cushion-like tufts of ascending squamules. Podetia sometimes present with an abruptly widening cup  which is distorted with lobules and usually has small brown apothecia.

P + red, K + y.

Habitat. Very common on acid soil or in small soil pockets and cracks on siliceous rocks in well-lit, rocky, coastal and upland areas.

C. subcervicornis x5

C. foliacea Primary thallus yellow-green, tufted, the squamules up to 0.8cm wide with deeply incised tips. Undersurface not pruinose but yellowish (this helps separate it from *C. subcervicornis* and *C. cervicornis*). Squamules frequently curled over to show the undersurface. Podetia rather rare and form a gradually widening irregular cup.
P + red, K−, KC + y.

Habitat. Widely distributed and often forms extensive patches particularly on basic, dry, sandy areas, stabilised shingle and grasslands near the coast; more rarely found inland (e.g., the Breckland).

C. foliacea x3

C. strepsilis Primary thallus buff to green-brown, shallowly notched at the tips. Podetia short and irregular but not normally present.

P + y, K−, C + bright green. This is the only British lichen to give this C + reaction (due to strepsilin).

Habitat. Locally abundant on well-lit peat moors.

C. strepsilis x4

PRIMARY THALLUS PERSISTENT.
Podetia simple, not terminating in a wide scyphus.
(see also *C. floerkeana* and *C. squamosa*)

C. coniocraea Primary thallus green, lower surface white, often forming extensive patches. Podetia slightly squamulose, becoming sorediate higher up, sometimes terminating in a narrow cup, but often horn-like.

P + r, K−.

Habitat. Very common in woods, where it is found on tree bases or decaying stumps and logs. It is resistant to pollution and is often the only *Cladonia* to be found near urban areas. Colour and K− reaction separate infertile material from *C. macilenta.*

C. coniocraea x5

C. ochrochlora Doubtfully distinct from the previous species, from which it differs in the longer podetia which are decorticate in patches and occasionally branched.

P + r, K−.

Habitat. Fairly common, usually in damper woods than *C. coniocraea.* Found on very rich humus, tree stumps, etc.

C. ochrochlora x4

PRIMARY THALLUS PERSISTENT, PODETIA SMALL AND BRANCHED
(See also *C. ochrochlora* and *Pycnothelia papillaria*)

C. parasitica Primary thallus a compact mat of much incised, small, delicate squamules, pale brownish-grey with granular soralia on the lower surface. Podetia are without a cup, mostly branched, contorted, furrowed and with soredia or squamules.

K + y, P + o.

Habitat. Frequent, particularly in the south east on tree stumps and damp humus.

C. parasitica x4

PODETIA WITH WELL DEVELOPED SCYPHI
(See also *C. crispata*)

C. chlorophaea Primary thallus greenish-grey, squamules small, broad, erect and incised. Undersuface white and visible where the squamules curl over. Podetia expand smoothly from the base to the wide cup. The outer surface and the interior of the cup is covered in rather granular soredia.

C

Due to the many chemotypes the reactions are unreliable but it is usually P + r.

Habitat. Very common on soil, rotting stumps and peat. The rarer *C. conistea* is chemically distinct and has farinose soralia.

C. chlorophaea x6

C. pyxidata Similar to the preceding species but differs in the rough, warted or squamulose surface to the podetia. There are no soredia. This species was used to produce a remedy for whooping cough.

P + r.

Habitat. Very common, often on drier more sandy soils than *C. chlorophaea*. *C. pocillum* is similar, but has adpressed rosettes of squamules, found on rocks, mortar and humus in calcareous sites.

C. pyxidata x4

C. fimbriata Similar to the preceding species in this group but distinguished by the slender stems to the podetia which open abruptly to a very regular cup. The podetia being "golf tee" shaped and covered in greenish farinose soredia P + r.

Habitat. Very common on rotting wood, earth and sand dunes, often amongst mosses.

C. fimbriata x3

PRIMARY SCYPHI HAVING SECONDARY SCYPHI PROLIFERATING FROM THEM

C. verticillata Squamules usually absent. Podetia very distinctive, dark green-brown, areolate, lighter between the areolae, opening abruptly into a wide shallow cup from the centre of which grow further podetia in tiers. *C. cervicornis* is now thought to represent a squamulose phase of this species. P + r.

Habitat. Frequent on acid soils, peat and sand dunes.

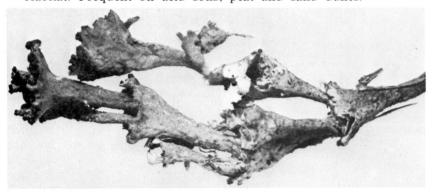

C. verticillata x5

C. squamosa Primary thallus often disappears early in development. Podetia very variable, with, either a poorly developed cup or one that widens out abruptly from the stem, the centre of the podetia is open, with the margin having digitate extensions, podetia covered in prominent grey to bright green squamules. It may be differentiated from *C. crispata* by the velvety appearance of the decorticated areas.

Reactions negative, but the variety *subsquamosa* is K + y, P + r.

Habitat. Very common on acid soil, peat and rotting wood particularly in sheltered situations.

C. squamosa x3

APOTHECIA RED

C. coccifera A very distinctive species in which the apothecia are persistently red. Squamules usually present, yellowish-green, incised with a white undersurface. Podetia short, stout, yellow-grey or yellow-green, covered in granular soralia and frequently small squamules. The scyphus is regular with bright red apothecia or pycnidia, often on stalks around the margin. The apothecia become confluent and may cover the whole of the top of the cup.

KC + y, P–.

Habitat. Very common on acid soil, rotting trees, heathland, sand dunes and soil pockets on walls in upland regions.

C. coccifera x2.5

C. gonecha [**C. sulphurina**] Primary squamules disappearing early. Podetia yellowish-grey, either without a scyphus or with a cup that expands gradually from the base. Podetia covered with farinose soralia except at the base, where it is corticate or occasionally squamulose. The cup margins usually have red pycnidia or apothecia often on short stalks. (*C. deformis* differs in the presence of zeorin and the absence of squamatic acid. It has more regular podetia with less distinct longitudinal grooves. It is very rare in Britain).

8

KC + y for both species.

Habitat. Very rare in the south but becomes common in Scotland, on rotting wood, humus and peat.

C. gonecha x3

C. floerkeana Primary squamules grey, very small and slightly incised, persistent and forming a thin mat. Podetia simple or branched, sometimes expanding at the apex to give the appearance of a scyphus. It is covered in grey squamules or has granular soralia on the upper part. The apothecia are dark red and confluent.

Reactions negative.

Habitat. Very common on rotting wood, humus, peat and sand dunes.

C. floerkeana x6

C. bellidiflora Primary squamules greyish-yellow and usually dying away. Podetia either without a scyphus or only a narrow cup, which may have secondary podetia growing around the rim. Apothecia bright red. It may be distinguished from *C. squamosa* by the red apothecia, yellow colour and the KC + y reaction.

Habitat. Frequent on soil and peat, mainly in upland areas of Scotland.

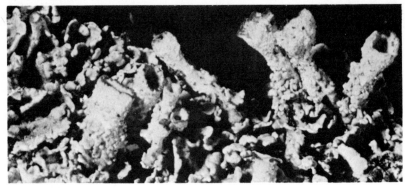

C. bellidiflora x6

C. polydactyla Primary squamules grey, up to 5mm high with incised tips. It usually persists as a thin mat. Podetia up to 5cm high, branched and lacking a scyphus, or with a regular scyphus which frequently has secondary podetia growing around its margin. The lower part of the podetia is squamulose

becoming farinose-sorediate higher up. Apothecia bright red. K + y, P + o.

Habitat. Very common on humus, soil and peat.

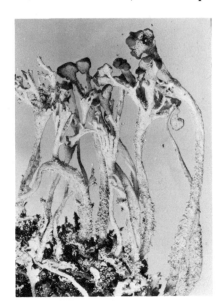

C. polydactyla x4

C. digitata Primary squamules large (up to about 6mm wide), grey-green with rounded lobes. Undersurface white becoming brown towards the base and covered with farinose soralia which extend right to the margin. Frequently infertile when it forms a loose mat of squamules. Podetia short with an  irregular cup which expands smoothly from the base and is covered with farinose soralia. Apothecia bright red. K + y, P + o.

Habitat. Frequent in the south on rotting trees, humus and peat.

C. digitata x2

C. macilenta Primary squamules small, green-grey, incised and often forming a dense mat which may not persist. Podetia simple or branched without a scyphus, the lower part squamulose, the upper part granular or farinose sorediate. Apothecia bright red. When not fertile may be separated from *C.*  *coniocraea* by its greyer colour and the K + y reaction.

Both species are P + orange.

Habitat. Common on rotting wood, fences and soil.

C. macilenta x5

COLLEMA The generic name is derived from the Greek for gelatine. The thallus is homoiomerous and is gelatinous and swollen when wet, becoming papery when dry. Apothecia lecanorine, the discs appearing reddish when dry. Spores variously shaped, septate or becoming muriform.
All reactions negative.

C. tenax x1750

1. Without isidia, abundant apothecia, on basic substrates
....**C. tenax**
Thallus with isidia or incised lobate margins.................2
2. Isidia globose...3
Isidia flattened or coralloid, or with lobate margins......5
3. Lobes smooth, with minute striations. Very swollen when wet, apothecia rare.....................................**C. auriculatum**
Thallus ridged or smooth, little swollen when wet.......4
4. Thallus ridged, rather adpressed, with numerous apothecia
....**C. nigrescens**
Thallus smooth, fairly erect. Apothecia rare **C. subfurvum**
5. Longitudinally ridged with coralloid isidia .**C. furfuraceum**
Lobes not longitudinally ridged. Lobes imbricate..........6
6. Lobes with flattened isidia, mainly in the centre
....**C. crispum**
Lobes with incised rather lobate margins......**C. cristatum**

CORTICOLOUS

(All species may rarely be found on basic rocks)

Collema furfuraceum Thallus very dark green or brown. A large species with lobes up to 4cm across and forming extensive colonies. The margins and tips of the lobes often curl upwards, the upper surface has conspicuous longitudinal ridges, along these ridges are often dense masses of coralloid isidia  which may cover the whole upper surface of mature lobes. Apothecia are very rare.

Habitat. Frequent, mainly in the west, on damp deciduous trees or moss on trees.

C. furfuraceum x5

C. nigrescens Thallus dark brown or green. It differs from the previous species in being more adpressed, with globular isidia and usually with numerous apothecia. Spores fusiform 5 + septate.

Habitat. Not rare in the west in similar situations to *C. furfuraceum.*

C. nigrescens x6

C. subfurvum [C. subflaccidum] Thallus dark brown, slightly lighter on the undersurface and at the tips of the lobes. More erect than the previous species with smaller globular isidia which frequently cover the thallus. Apothecia are very rare.

Habitat. Frequent on deciduous trees and tree stumps.

C. subfurvum x10

TERRICOLOUS OR SAXICOLOUS
(see also preceding species)

C. tenax Thallus dark greenish–black. Lobes up to 3cm across, erect, lacking isidia, crowded or often obscured by the very numerous apothecia. Apothecia about 2mm diam. Spores 8 per ascus, muriform.

Habitat. Common on basic earth, sand, and mortar in walls.

C. tenax x10

C. auriculatum Thallus dark brown. Lobes up to 3cm across, very swollen when wet, erect and covered with coarse globular isidia that arise in discrete patches and sometimes cover the thallus (a few isidia are sometimes found on the lower surface). The lobes are smooth and undulating except for minute striations. Apothecia are rare.

Habitat. Common on hard calcareous rocks often amongst mosses in shaded sites, sometimes on the ground in chalk or limestone grasslands.

C. auriculatum x3

79

C. crispum Thallus brown-black, lobes under 1cm across, thick and imbricate. Isidia flattened and mainly confined to the centre of the thallus. Apothecia about 2mm diam often irregular in shape with a thin margin. Spores becoming muriform.

Habitat. Common on calcareous rocks, walls, mortar and more rarely on basic soils.

C. crispum x6

C. cristatum Thallus brown-black, lobes to 1cm across, rather thin with deeply incised margins that may appear lobulate. A few flattened isidia are sometimes found towards the centre of the lobe. Apothecia are not infrequent. Spores muriform.

Habitat. Common on calcareous rocks, mortar or sometimes on soil.

C. cristatum x3

CONIOCYBE The name is probably derived from the Greek for dust. Thallus crustose to almost leprose. The apothecia are borne on the end of long stalks. The asci disintegrate leaving the spores in a loose powdery mass that easily rubs off (a mazaedium). Spores, yellow to pale brown, simple, spherical, 8 per ascus, minute (2—4µm).

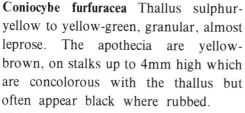

C. furfuracea x600

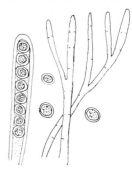

Coniocybe furfuracea Thallus sulphur-yellow to yellow-green, granular, almost leprose. The apothecia are yellow-brown, on stalks up to 4mm high which are concolorous with the thallus but often appear black where rubbed.
Habitat. Rather rare with apothecia. Found in the south and west, mainly in upland regions in siliceous rock crevices or on roots and tree stumps. Often found sterile when it is difficult to separate from sterile *Lecidea lucida* except by chromotography.

C. furfuracea x30

CORISCIUM This genus is probably a member of the *Basidiomycotina*. It appears to be an association between an alga and a fungus of the genus *Omphalina* which produces toadstool-shaped fruiting bodies. There is only one species.

x4

Coriscium viride Thallus glaucous-green, consisting of circular squamules with raised margins. They resemble *Normandina pulchella* but are larger (up to about 3mm diam) and do not have soredia. The fruiting body is toadstool-shaped, several millimetres high and about 1cm diam.

Habitat. Not infrequent on wet peat moors in western Scotland but also found in southern England.

C. viride x8

CORNICULARIA The name is probably derived from the latin for a little horn. Thallus fruticose, hard and spiny when dry. Apothecia lecanorine but usually absent in British specimens, except for *C. normoerica.* The shape of the pseudocyphellae is important in identification but the chemical reactions

C. aculeata x600

are all negative (except for the very rare *C. divergens* which has a C + red medulla). They may be distinguished from species of *Cladonia* by their darker colour.

1. Thallus dull brown-black, erect, on exposed rocks, no pseudocyphellae ....**C. normoerica**
    Thallus shiny brown, forming scattered or interwoven mats 2
2. Forms loose mats, pseudocyphellae in depressions...........
    ....**C. aculeata**
    Forms dense spiky tufts, pseudocyphellae flat **C. muricata**

Cornicularia aculeata Thallus chestnut to dark brown, glossy, up to 5cm high. Branches somewhat flattened, usually with white pseudocyphellae in depressions, especially near the axils. The branches terminate in short blunt spines which may also be present on the main branches. It may be scattered or form interwoven mats. Apothecia are very rare. Habitat. Very common on heaths and sand dunes.

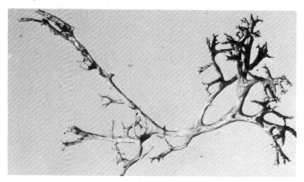

C. aculeata x5

C. muricata This is very similar to the previous species but is more densely branched, with the branching often at a narrower angle. The pseudocyphellae are not in depressions. It forms very dense mats that are very easily detached from the substrate.

Habitat. As *C. aculeata* but less common. It is often found on mineral spoil-heaps.

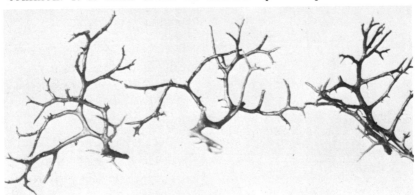

C. muricata x4

C. normoerica Thallus matt brown-black, erect and up to 5cm high, slightly dichotomously branched, the branches usually flattened. Apothecia very common, terminal or sub-terminal often with a spiny margin.

Habitat. Locally common in upland areas, on coarse grained siliceous rocks.

C. normoerica x4

CYPHELIUM Thallus crustose. Apothecia lecanorine but when mature the asci break down to form a loose mass of spores (a mazaedium) which rubs off on the finger. Spores brown, one septate.

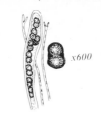

C. inquinans x300

Cyphelium inquinans Thallus pale grey, and warted. Apothecia are usually present, up to 2mm diam, innate or sessile, irregular in shape, often with a white pruinose margin. May be distinguished from *Lecidea* species by the soot like mark left on the finger from a mature apothecium and by the one septate spores.

Habitat. Common on exposed old fence posts and more rarely on old oaks in south-east Britain. It is rare in the Scottish Highlands on decorticate pines.

C. inquinans x8

CYSTOCOLEUS Thallus filamentous with *Trentepohlia* filaments being enveloped by the fungal hyphae. There is only one species (or possibly two) and it is only found sterile.

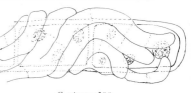

C. niger x200

Cystocoleus niger Thallus of a dense black felted mass of filaments, often with *Racodium rupestre*. The surrounding fungal hyphae are contorted and wavy unlike *R. rupestre* where they are straight.

Habitat. Common on shaded vertical siliceous rocks in upland areas.

C. niger x15

DERMATOCARPON Thallus foliose or squamulose. Perithecia immersed in the thallus but the ostiole is usually clearly visible. Spores, simple, colourless, 8 per ascus. Some species have been gathered and used as food in Asia.

D. hepaticum x350

1. Compact mat of thick lobes, acid rock, stream, river or lake margins ....**D. fluviatile**
   Lobes not thick and a compact mat, on soil or rock ..2
2. Thallus red-brown, of adpressed, often overlapping squamules up to 1cm across. On soil..........**D. hepaticum**
   Thallus pale grey to grey-brown, larger, not overlapping, attached by central holdfast. On rock...............**D. miniatum**

Dermatocarpon fluviatile Thallus green-brown when wet, grey when dry; thick, consisting of a compact mat of erect contorted lobes. The upper surface pitted with the dark brown ostioles of the perithecia. Undersurface lighter brown, darker towards the centre.

Habitat. Frequent on siliceous rocks and boulders on the margins of nutrient-deficient streams and lakes in upland areas, where it is submerged from time to time.

Dimer
greenis
Apoth
diam,
translu
makes
Habita
decidu
areas
someti

D. fluviatale x3

D. hepaticum Thallus buff to reddish brown with dark brown ostioles. Undersurface black and felted. Forms discrete, adpressed squamules up to 1cm across, often with fine crenulations or slightly raised edges. It may form colonies several cms across.

Habitat. Frequent on calcareous soils, especially in crevices in hard calcareous rocks, sometimes on walls amongst mosses.

D

D. dil
previou
about (
Habitat
conifer:
and otl

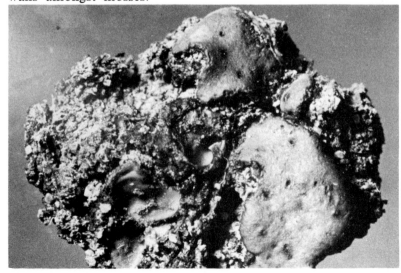

D. hepaticum x9

D. diluta

DIPLOSCHISTES Thallus crustose. Apothecia urceolate, lecanorine. Spores becoming dark, muriform when mature, usually 8 per ascus. Close to *Thelotrema* but the proper margin is far less prominent. The C + r reaction helps to separate these species from *Lecanora* (*Aspicilia*) and *Cyphelium inquinans*.

D. scruposus x350

Thallus smooth, lead-coloured, regularly cracked areolate, maritime ....**D. caesioplumbeus**
Thallus matt, thick, warted not aereolate,grey. On mosses, walls or rocks...**D. scruposus**

Diploschistes scruposus Thallus leaden grey, thick, warted. Apothecia usually numerous, discs black, deeply immersed at first, sometimes with a noticeable proper margin, becoming more open as they develop, often pruinose. Spores colourless at first and appearing 5-7 septate, becoming muriform and sometimes very dark.
K + y, C + r.

5

·C

Habitat. Common on rocks and walls. Particularly over mosses on limestone and mortar *(D. bryophilus).*

D. scruposus x8

D. caesioplumbeus Thallus mid to dark leaden grey, cracked areolate, slightly shiny. Apothecia immersed several often found in each areole. The proper margin being clearly seen in the young apothecia. Mature apothecia mainly pruinose and under 0.5mm diam. Spores becoming dark muriform.
K −, C + r.

Habitat. Frequent on well-lit siliceous rocks in the supralittoral zone in the south-west.

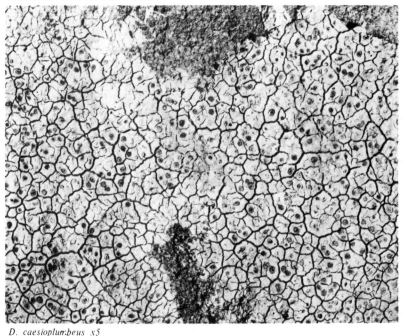

D. caesioplumbeus x5

DIRINA Thallus crustose, fruiting bodies lirellate. Spores colourless, 3-8 septate, 8 per ascus. This is a mainly tropical and sub-tropical genus that just extends in range to Britain. The C + rose − red reaction and the orange colouration (caused by the presence of the orange phycobiont *Trentepohlia*) on scratched surfaces, help to identify this genus (but also found in some other genera e.g. *Opegrapha*).

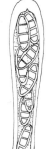

D. repanda x500

91

Dirina stenhammarii (Lecanactis stenhammarii) Thallus almost white to light grey, thick, areolate, determinate at the margins with a white prothallus. Small (about 0.5mm) globose, mounds of farinose soredia are scattered over the thallus, these may spread to form a complete crust. Not fertile in Britain.

The very rare *D. repanda* lacks soralia and may in fact be a fertile counterpart. *Arthonia lobata* is superficially similar but is thinner and lacks the pink colouration.

K −, C + rose -red. A scratched surface shows yellow-orange.
Habitat. Locally abundant in south-west on vertical calcareous rocks, it is also frequent on walls of churches in the south.

D. stenhammarii x6

ENTEROGRAPHA Thallus crustose, usually with a black prothallus. Fruiting bodies immersed and forming lines or appearing as simple perithecia. Spores colourless, multiseptate, 8 per ascus.

x600

E. crassa x300

Enterographa crassa Thallus very variable, usually brown or dull olive green, thick, areolate, frequently forming neat mosaics divided by the black prothallus. Apothecia dark brown, in the form of small, fine, thread-like lines or dots, often more crowded towards the edge of the thallus.

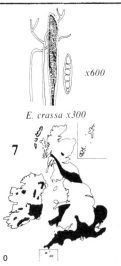

Habitat. A very common species on shaded trees, often forming very extensive colonies. Exceptionally it is found on damp shaded acid rocks, where grey to black specimens with roughly rectangular apothecia are probably the rare *E. hutchinsiae.*

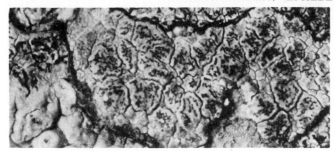

E. crassa x9

EPHEBE Thallus fruticose, filamentous. In mature strands of the thallus, the fungal hyphae are mixed in with the blue-green algal cells. Apothecia immersed and formed at globose enlargements of the thallus, either as shown or in slight swellings. Spores colourless, simple to 3 septate, 8 per ascus.

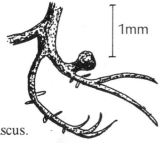

1mm

Ephebe lanata Thallus dark green to black, soft and filamentous forming small mats up to about 1cm across. The filaments much divided (often dichotomously), tapering to fine points. The thallus is somewhat thickened in places and some of the branchlets may form holdfasts that adhere to the substrate. Apothecia rare in Britain, very small, often in groups in swellings formed on the branches. Spores simple becoming 1 septate or very rarely 2 septate.

Distinguished from *Alectoria pubescens* by its softer texture, the presence of blue-green algae and the different habitat. The rare **E. hispidula** has small branchlets and is illustrated above. Habitat. Not rare in upland regions on damp rocks near acidic streams and waterfalls, in the splash zone.

E. lanata x9

EVERNIA Thallus flattened and attached at one point so that it appears to be fruticose, but as the algal layer is only found under the upper cortex and the lower surface is differentiated from the upper, it is actually foliose. Apothecia lecanorine, spores simple, colourless, 8 per ascus. There is only one British species.

Evernia prunastri Thallus strap-shaped, pendent, yellow to green-grey above, white-cottony underneath. This light undersurface separates it from *Ramalina* species which are approximately the same colour all round. It usually feels fairly soft, lobes strongly flattened, upper surface with net-like ridges that become sorediate in larger specimens (about 3cm long). Very rarely fertile, discs dark brown, concave to plane.

Habitat. Very common on deciduous trees, rarely on rocks or stabilised sand dunes. It is more tolerant of pollution than *Ramalina* species and may be found in a very stunted form in regions of moderate pollution. It becomes much rarer in Scotland. It has been used extensively by man for many purposes including; as "oak moss", a fixative for perfume, as a dyeing agent, ground up to make a hair powder and as wadding in shotguns. The usnic acid it contains can be used to produce an antibiotic but it has also been known to produce an allergy in woodcutters. Long-tailed tits greatly favour this species to line their nests.

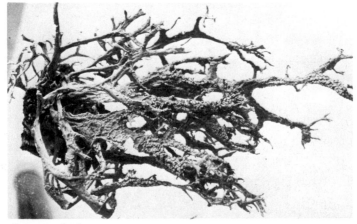

E. prunastri x2

FULGENSIA Thallus crustose, placodioid, and in shades of yellow. Apothecia lecanorine. Spores colourless, simple (may appear 1 septate due to the more solid material gathering at the ends). 8 per ascus. This genus was removed from *Caloplaca* due to the simple spores.

K + purple.

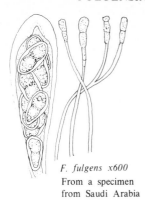

F. *fulgens* x600
From a specimen from Saudi Arabia

Fulgensia fulgens Thallus egg-yellow, pruinose, consisting of rosettes of small (about 1-2mm) adpressed, very convex, imbricate incised squamules. The thallus is lobate around the margins and up to 3cm diam. Apothecia fairly small (up to about 1.5mm), orange, the thin thalline margin being excluded early. Spores simple but may appear 1 septate.

K + purple. Its pale yellow and white egg-like appearance, habitat, and simple spores help to separate it from *Caloplaca*. Habitat. Not rare in the south-west on mosses and soil on calcareous dunes, it also occurs in a few sites on the calcareous soils of East Anglia such as Breckland.

F. *fulgens* x5

GRAPHINA Thallus crustose, sometimes nearly immersed. Apothecia, lirellae with carbonaceous margins. Spores colourless, muriform, 8 per ascus. Due to their resemblance to writing the Graphidacae are amongst the earliest records that can be identified as lichens.

G. anguina x800

Graphina anguina Thallus grey, usually wrinkled and cracked, slightly shiny, sometimes leprose. Apothecia immersed, the thalline margin often slightly pushed upwards, the carbonaceous centre is flat and often pruinose. Lirellae are short and usually stellate. May be distinguished from the very similar *Phaeographis dendritica* by its shorter muriform spores. This is the only lichen genus with lirellae and colourless muriform spores, but beware of the common British fungal genus *Gloniopsis* which has these features.

Habitat. Not rare especially in the South and West, on somewhat shaded often smooth–barked trees.

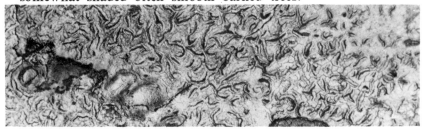

G. anguina x8

GRAPHIS Thallus crustose. Apothecia, lirellae with pronounced emergent carbonaceous margins up to several mm long. Spores colourless (occasionally some spores become slightly coloured), multiseptate, 8 per ascus. Usually much larger than in *Opegrapha* but small specimens may be separated by the longer spores.

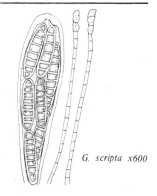

G. scripta x600

Margins of lirellae with several furrows.......... **G. elegans**
Margins of lirellae unfurrowed..........................**G. scripta**

Graphis elegans Thallus grey, smooth and slightly shiny, or wrinkled. Apothecia very varied in shape and size but always with the carbonaceous margins raised above the thallus and almost meeting in the centre of the lirella. Each margin has a number of longitudinal furrows. Spores colourless, 7-12 septate.

Habitat. Widespread on smooth–barked trees and twigs.

G. elegans x6

G. scripta Thallus grey, smooth or wrinkled. Apothecia very variable but with raised, unfurrowed, carbonaceous margins. The centre of the lirellae are sometimes pruinose. Spores colourless, 7-10 septate. Many varieties have been named but most are of little significance and in a number of cases are due only to the growth of the host.

Habitat. Very common on smooth–barked trees and twigs.

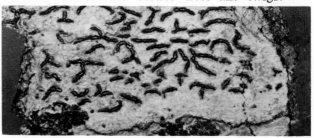

G. scripta x6

GYALECTA Thallus crustose or nearly absent. Apothecia lecideine, not immersed, with a prominent orange or yellow pseudothalline margin, disc concave (the generic name is derived from the Greek for concave). Spores colourless, septate or muriform, 8 per ascus.

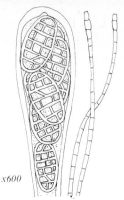

G. truncigena x600

Apothecia pink, on hard limestone, spores 3 septate ....**G. jenensis**
Apothecia pale orange, on deciduous trees, spores 5 + septate ....**G. truncigena**

Gyalecta truncigena Thallus grey, thin and slightly powdery. Apothecia very small (about 0.5mm), orange or flesh-coloured with a thick, paler margin. Spores 5-7 septate usually with one or two parallel longitudinal septa.

Habitat. Not rare but easily overlooked. Found on shaded rough—barked deciduous trees (especially elm), mainly in the south and west, (var. *derivata* has more than 7 septate spores and *G. flotowii* has smaller almost elliptical spores with erratically angled septa).

G. truncigena x10

G. jenensis Thallus light grey, thin, matt. Apothecia with orange discs and a thick margin that may become slightly dentate, and looking like the edge of a pie crust. Spores 3 septate but becoming muriform (the spores of the superficially similar *Petractis clausa* are persistently 3 septate and the apothecia more dentate).

5

0

Habitat. Rather rare but locally abundant on shaded hard limestone. It is also found in the south especially on basic rocks near the sea, it may spread on to adjacent mosses.

G. jenensis x9

GYALECTINA Thallus crustose. Apothecia lecideine and often immersed, becoming convex when mature. Spores persistently septate, never muriform, 8-16 per ascus. This is mainly a tropical genus growing on trees and leaves. There is only one species in Europe.

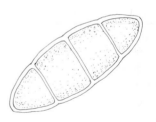

G. carneolutea x2000

Gyalectina carneolutea [Cryptolechia carneolutea] Thallus light grey, thin, matt. Apothecia about 1mm diam, translucent orange, with margins that become dentate or excluded. Spores 3 septate.

9

C

Habitat. Rare in the extreme south and south-west, at one time north to the Isle of Man. Found on shaded ash and elm trees. It is very rare on limestone whilst the superficially similar *Petractis clausa* is always found on limestone.

THALLUS LOBATE AT THE MARGIN
(Subgenus *Placodium*)

Lecanora muralis Thallus greenish-grey to yellow-grey, large (up to about 10cm across) and consisting of small lobules 1 to 2mm wide which are often pruinose around their edges. The outer margin of the thallus becomes clearly lobate. Usually fertile the numerous apothecia having brown discs. The margin often  becomes broken when mature. The apothecia are confined to the centre of the thallus where they are crowded together and are often angular in shape.

Habitat. Very common on man-made substrates except in the west and north. It is one of the more pollution resistant species and is even found near the centre of large towns on basic substrates such as asbestos-cement (it is less common on the less well-lit, damper north side of roofs). It is rarer in its natural habitat of bird perching sites in upland areas.

L. muralis x5

NOT PLACODIOID, APOTHECIA INNATE
(Subgenus *Aspicilia*)

L. calcarea [Aspicilia calcarea] Thallus white, smooth and usually divided into areolae, often surrounded by a grey or white prothallus. Apothecia irregular in shape, one or more in the centre of an areola, disc black often pruinose with a distinct overarching margin which frequently disappears as the apothecium matures.

Habitat. Common on hard calcareous rocks, walls and tombstones.

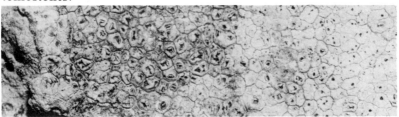

L. calcarea x6

L. lacustris [Aspicilia lacustris] A distinctive species with an orange thallus which is smooth and slightly cracked. Usually fertile with small (less than 0.4mm) innate apothecia, discs orange to brown, concave becoming plane.

Habitat. Common on inundated siliceous rocks, by streams and lakes in upland regions.

L. lacustris x6

APOTHECIA NOT INNATE
(Subgenus *Lecanora*)
Saxicolous

L. atra Thallus light to medium grey, smooth or warted, sometimes with a thin prothallus. Usually fertile, mainly with the apothecia in the more central part of the thallus. Apothecia with thick margins and convex black discs. When mature the apothecia become plane with a contorted or crenulate margin. If cut open the thecium is purple–brown. K + y.

Habitat. Very common throughout Britain on well-lit siliceous rocks and walls, it is rarely found on trees.

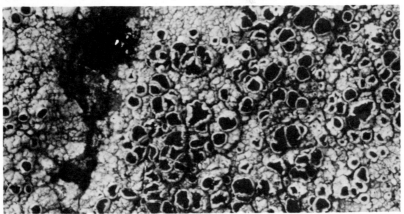

L. atra x3

L. gangaleoides Very similar to the preceding species but the thallus is frequently a darker greenish-grey and more warted. The discs of the apothecia are persistently convex and the margins do not usually become contorted. If cut open the thecium is dark green-brown. K + y.

Habitat. As *L. atra* but often out of direct sunlight, more common near the sea and prefering rather less basic sites.

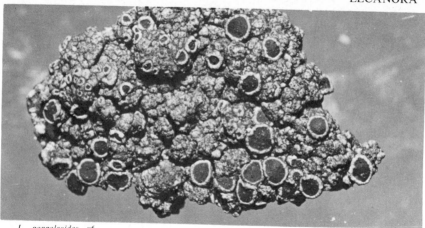

L. gangaleoides x6

L. campestris Thallus grey, warted or areolate with a white prothallus. Usually fertile with the apothecia crowded in the centre. Apothecia large (up to about 2mm), discs chestnut to dark red-brown with a smooth margin that becomes contorted in mature apothecia. K + y.

Habitat. Very common on somewhat basic to calareous substrates, tombstones and walls.

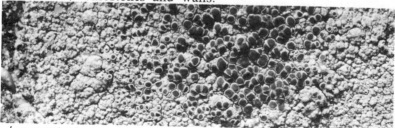

L. campestris x3

L. helicopsis Thallus leaden to yellow grey, smooth and cracked or slightly warted. Apothecia sessile, less than 1mm diam, very dark brown with a margin which becomes excluded. K − .

Habitat. Very common on exposed siliceous rocks just above high–water mark.

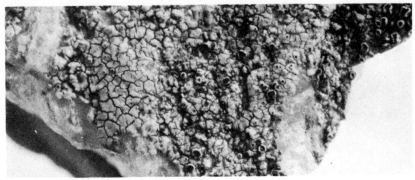

L. helicopsis x5

L. actophila Thallus creamy–white to grey, smooth, areolate, often with a white prothallus. Apothecia less than 1mm diam, green-black with an entire margin which becomes contorted but not excluded as in *L. helicopsis*.
K −.
Habitat. Very common in similar habitats to *L. helicopsis*.

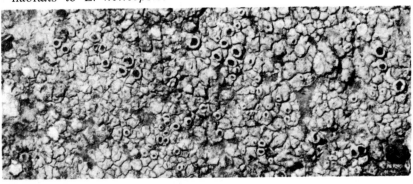

L. actophila x8

L. rupicola Thallus light grey, thick, smooth and cracked. Apothecia more innate than with the two preceding species. Discs pinkish-buff and pruinose, convex and contorted when mature.
K + y. Apothecia C + y.
Habitat. Very common in similar situations to the preceding two species but also not uncommon inland, in upland areas.

6

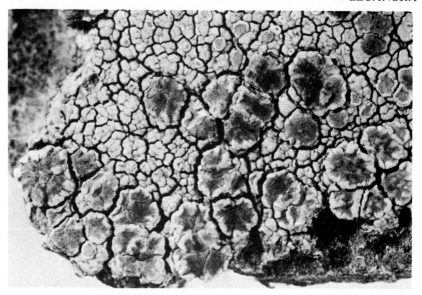

L. rupicola x10

L. badia Thallus brown, thick, smooth and shiny, or warted. Apothecia up to 2mm diam, discs brown becoming convex when mature, with an entire margin that is often contorted or crenulate. Apothecia often very crowded on the thallus. The spores are a very distinctive shape that separates it from other *Lecanora* species.

Habitat. Frequent in upland areas on hard siliceous rocks, also on walls, less frequently on coastal rocks.

L. badia spore x1200

L. badia x6

L. dispersa Thallus very light grey or white, thin or evanescent. In very polluted areas it becomes dark green-black (form *dissipata*). In unpolluted regions on calcareous substrates there is a granular placodioid form (form *albescens*). Apothecia small, usually less than 1mm diam, pale greenish-grey to dark brown. Margin entire, and often pruinose when young, becoming slightly crenulate.

Habitat. Very common and found even in the centres of cities on nutrient-rich, basic substrates. In unpolluted areas it is also found on nutrient-rich bark and a wide range of other substrates such as siliceous rocks, iron, leather, etc.

L. dispersa x4

L. crenulata Very similar to the previous species but with smaller apothecia (up to about 0.5mm diam), with a brown persistently pruinose disc and a more crenulate margin than *L. dispersa*.

Habitat. Occasional in unpolluted regions but usually only on hard calcareous rocks and walls.

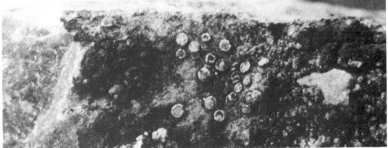

L. crenulata x8

L. polytropa Thallus yellow-green often of scattered granules with a dark prothallus, often crowded together in cracks in the substrate. Usually fertile with the apothecia sometimes obscuring the surface of the thallus. Apothecia small (less than 0.5mm diam), greenish-brown. The mature apothecia become strongly convex and exclude the margin.

Habitat. Common in less polluted areas on acid rocks, walls and stabilized shingle. It is occasionally found on sawn wood by railways, harbours, etc.

L. polytropa x10

L. intricata Similar to the previous species with a yellow-green thallus which may be scattered or if thicker, almost squamulose. Apothecia dark green-brown and not becoming convex, more innate than *L. polytropa*.

Habitat. Occasional in similar habitats to *L. polytropa*. The common var.

soralifera [L. soralifera] has a similar thallus and is usually sterile but has numerous bright yellow-green soralia scattered over the thallus. It is frequent on siliceous rocks, especially in the southern Pennines and N. Yorkshire.

L. intricata var. *soralifera* x6

CORTICOLOUS

L. chlarotera Thallus grey, smooth or warted, sometimes areolate. Apothecia usually numerous, buff to red-brown, sometimes piebald (due to parasitic fungi of the genus *Vouauxiella*). Angular crystals are found in the thick, smooth (or slightly crenulate) margins of the large (up to 2mm diam) apothecia.

Thallus K + fy. Margins of apothecia P ·
Habitat. Very common on trees in unpolluted areas. It is the only common species with red-brown discs and a P − margin. *L. chlarona* has smaller (about 1mm diam) apothecia with a P + o margin and is not infrequent in upland regions on conifers and sawn wood. (The rarer *L. intumescens* is found on deciduous smooth-barked trees and has a thick, smooth margin that is P + y)

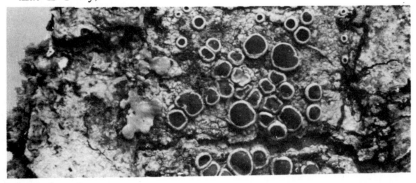

L. chlarotera x7

L. pallida Thallus pale grey to almost white, smooth or warted, often with a white prothallus. Apothecia up to about 1mm diam. Disc buff to pale mud-colour, usually densely pruinose. Margins entire but becoming crenulate or excluded in mature apothecia. Thallus K + y, margin C − , P + r.

Habitat. Frequent on twigs, mainly of smooth-barked trees, but it is often small and easily overlooked.

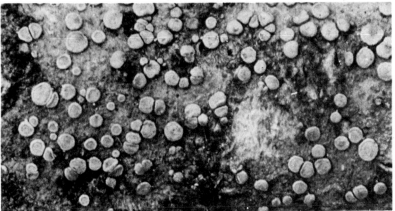

L. pallida x8

L. conizaeoides Thallus grey-green, thick and granular-sorediate, often forming a thick areolate crust that may cover extensive areas. Apothecia with greenish-buff to flesh-coloured (when dry) discs, with slightly crenulate margins which become covered in similar granules to the thallus.

Thallus P + r.

Habitat. Possibly the commonest British lichen. It is found mainly on trees, but sometimes also on walls, rocks or soil. It was a very rare species until this century, but it is very resistant to sulphur dioxide pollution and has replaced most other lichens near the centres of industrial areas. It is still a rare species in un-polluted regions, where it is usually found on twigs and fences.

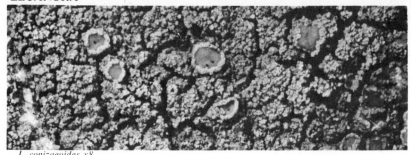

L. conizaeoides x8

L. expallens Thallus yellow-grey to green-grey with farinose soralia which may cover the thallus in an areolate crust. Usually found sterile. Apothecia very small (less than 0.5mm diam) with flesh – coloured discs and sorediate margins. When sterile it is difficult to separate from *Lecidea quernea* which has a slightly more ochre-green thallus and often a distinct grey prothallus.

Thallus K + fy, C + o.

Habitat. Very common on the trunks and stumps of trees, fences and on decorticated wood.

L. expallens x12

L. confusa Thallus yellow-grey to green-grey, slightly granular to areolate. Usually fertile. Apothecia small (less than 0.75mm diam), greenish flesh colour with a pale margin that stands out brightly against the thallus. This margin however frequently becomes excluded. It is similar to *L. expallens* but lacks soralia and has a more scanty thallus.

Thallus K − (usually), C + o.

Habitat. Common in unpolluted areas on trees and fences.

L. confusa x12

L. jamesii Thallus light to mid grey, thin and often slightly wrinkled, with scattered, yellow-green, punctiform soralia. Apothecia rare with small green-brown discs. When sterile, it may be separated from *Haematomma elatinum* as that species has greyish lemon-yellow soralia that become confluent and a K + y thallus and P + o soralia. Thallus K − . Soralia P − .

Habitat. Not uncommon on trees in sheltered damp areas.

L. jamesii x6

LECIDEA The largest British genus. Many of the species are rare and difficult to separate except by microscopic examination. Thallus crustose or squamulose. Apothecia lecideine (lacking a thalline margin), usually with a dark coloured disc. Spores colourless, simple, usually 8 per ascus. There have been

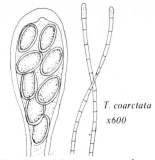

T. coarctata
x600

many recent changes of nomenclature affecting this genus and the following genera are included under *Lecidea* in this book. *Fuscidea, Huilia, Psora, Trapelia* and *Tremolechia Hypocenomyce, Protoblastenia.*

1.   Thallus at least in part squamulose 2
     Thallus crustose...5
2.   C + red 3
     C − 4
3a. Thallus white or grey, crustose in centre with squamulose margins. Acid soil near the sea.....................**L. wallrothii**
 b. Thallus grey-brown to green-brown, overlapping convex squamules, with sorediate tips. Fences, burnt wood, trees and bricks...**L. scalaris**
 c. Thin crust of scattered white to grey squamules**T. coarctata**
4.   Thallus pink with white pruinose margins to squamules K + mauve. Calcareous and upland soils.......**L. decipiens**
     Thallus green to dark chestnut, margins not pruinose, calcareous soils K −...**L. lurida**
5.   Saxicolous or corticolous...6
     Terricolous, muscicolous or lingicolous..........................18
6.   Saxicolous 7
     Corticolous...17
7.   Thallus yellow-grey to sulphur-yellow.............................8
     Thallus grey, brown or rust-red 10
8.   Thallus yellow-grey to yellow-green, thick, cracked, not sorediate ....**L. sulphurea**
     Thallus sorediate...9

9. Thallus sulphur to lemon – yellow comprising only a sorediate crust..**L. lucida**

Thallus green-yellow to yellow-grey, thick, areolate. Concolorous soralia on areolate margins or covering the areolae ....**L. orosthea**

10. Apothecia to 4mm diam, convex. May have blue-grey punctiform soralia and then usually infertile...............11

Apothecia to 1mm diam, not sorediate......................13

11. Thallus white to grey or rusty. Apothecia blue-white pruinose 12

Thallus grey or rusty. Apothecia not pruinose . **H. macrocarpa**

12. Thallus with blue-grey soralia, often infertile....**L. tumida**

Thallus lacks soralia, usually fertile.....**H. albocaerulescens**

13. Thallus pale grey with web-like black prothallus; apothecia to 1mm. On siliceous pebbles..........................**L. erratica**

Thallus grey and warted or scattered; or grey to brown or rust-red, smooth and/or areolate 14

14. Thallus rust red. Apothecia innate.....................**T. atrata**

Thallus grey to brown. Apothecia innate to sessile.....15

15. Thallus C + r, thin crust or scattered squamules, no prothallus ....**T. coarctata**

Thallus C –, areolate, black prothallus between and around areolae...16

16. Medulla P + r. Apothecia almost sessile, margin persistent ....**F. cyathoides**

Medulla P–. Apothecia innate, lacking a margin...**L. kochiana**

17. Thallus grey, soralia lenticular, yellow-buff C –, P + r ....**L. cinnabarina**

Thallus yellow-grey, farinose concolorous soralia C + o, P – ....**L. quernea**

18. Thallus dark brown, shiny, of isidiate-like granules. C – ....**L. uliginosa**

Thallus white, grey or yellowish, warted. C + r.........19

19. Thallus grey to green-grey with yellowish soralia ....**L. granulosa**

Thallus white to pale grey, sometimes pruinose, not sorediate..**L. wallrothii**

THALLUS CRUSTOSE
SAXICOLOUS

Fuscidea cyathoides (Lecidea cyathoides)
Thallus colour variable from light grey to a warm mousey–brown, areolate, smooth or rough, limited by a black prothallus that is also visible between the areolae. Apothecia sessile, small (up to 1 mm diam) dark brown or black. The disc becomes convex and the thin, paler proper margin is often excluded. Spores bean shaped. Medulla P + red. (The similar and even more upland *L. kochiana* has innate fruits and the medulla is P−). Habitat. Very common on hard siliceous rock and rarely on walls, in upland areas.

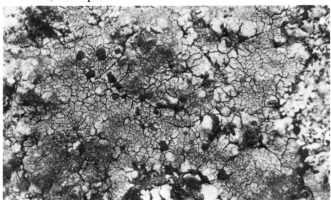

F. cyathoides
spore x1200

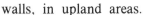

F. cyathoides x3

Lecidea sulphurea Thallus yellow-grey to bright yellow-green. Thick, warted and cracked. Often limited by a black prothallus which is also visible in the cracks. Apothecia usually present, when young, pale yellow or concolorous with the thallus but becoming convex, black with a pale grey pruina and an irregular shape. The somewhat similar *L. orosthea* differs in the sorediate margins of the areolae.
Habitat. Very common on siliceous rocks and walls.

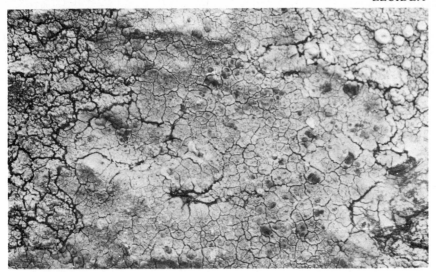

L. sulphurea x3

Trapelia coarctata (Lecidea coarctata)
Thallus light grey, consisting of a thin crust of scattered areolae and sometimes even slightly squamulose (then *T. ornata*). There is no prominent prothallus. Often sterile, apothecia often have a pseudomargin when young. Disc reddish-brown.

Thallus C + r.

Habitat. Common on siliceous rocks and walls and it may spread onto soil. Prefers damp situations and is often found in the damper shallow depressions in rocks.

T. coarctata x8

Huilia macrocarpa (Lecidea macrocarpa) Thallus thin or cracked, grey or often splashed rusty-red. There is a black prothallus. Apothecia prominent and large (up to 4 mm diam), the margin becomes excluded and the disc hard and rather globose, it lacks pruina.

Habitat. Frequent on acid rock, especially if damp, but prefers drier conditions than *H. albocaerulescens.*

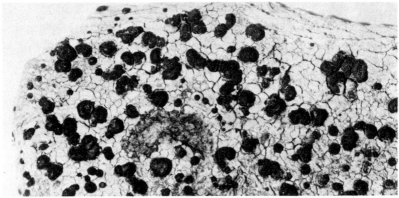

H. macrocarpa   x6

Tremolechia atrata (Lecidea dicksonii) Thallus a deep rust-red not splashed a rusty-colour as is often found in the preceding species and it also differs in the small concave areas of the nearly areolate thallus and small innate fruits that are found between the areolae.

Habitat. Fairly common in upland regions.

T. atrata x5

H. albocaerulescens (**Lecidea albocaerulescens**) Thallus grey, cracked but smooth. The apothecia differ from those of the previous species in having a blue-grey pruina and are irregularly convex.

Habitat. Common in similar habitats to *H. macrocarpa* but more especially in damper situations and may even be in the splash zone of streams.

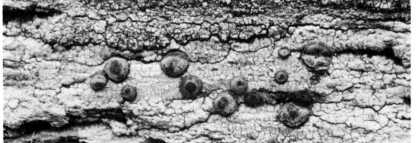

H. albocaerulescens x4

L. tumida Thallus white to pale grey, continuous or of scattered granules. Bluish-grey, punctiform soralia are scattered over the surface. Apothecia rare, large (to 2mm) becoming convex, black with a white pruina.

Habitat. Common on acid rocks. When fertile it may be separated from *H. albocaerulescens* by the presence of soralia.

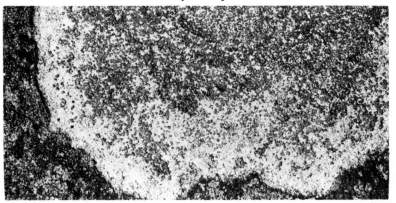

L. tumida x5

L. erratica Thallus pale grey, very thin and often of small scattered patches with apothecia or studded with dark pycnidia and surrounded by a dark grey prothallus. Apothecia small (less than 1mm diam) dark brown to black, often leaving a dark ring when the apothecia fall out.

Habitat. Not rare on siliceous pebbles on fixed shingle beaches in the east and south west.

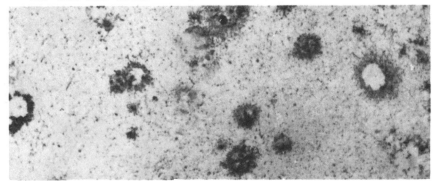

L. erratica x10

L. lucida Thallus bright sulphur-yellow to a lemon-emerald, granular and sorediate. Apothecia rare with pale lemon-green discs.

Habitat. Very common on shaded rocks and bricks especially where it is damp. Very rarely found on trees. Its distinctive colour is such that it can be

recognised at a distance. It is, however, difficult to separate from sterile *Coniocybe furfuracea,* which is usually found on trees and soil.

L. lucida x1

TERRICOLOUS, MUSCICOLOUS OR LIGNICOLOUS

L. granulosa Thallus granular greenish-grey and warted. Usually sterile with lighter yellow-green or yellow-brown soralia. Apothecia flesh-pink to dark brown, lacking pruina.
Cortex and soralia C + r.
Habitat. Common on peat, acid soil and rotting wood, often covering areas 10

cm or more across. It has even been found growing on an old damp boot and is one of the first species to recolonise the peat and heathland after a fire.

L. granulosa x6

L. uliginosa Thalius dark brown, consisting of compacted, small, shiny, convex, granules. Apothecia black, very small (less than 0.5 mm) with a paler margin that occasionally may become excluded.
Habitat. As *L. granulosa,* with which it is frequently found, especially on newly burnt moorland.

L. uliginosa x8

L. wallrothii Thallus white or pale grey, sometimes pruinose, thick and warted in the centre but appearing squamulose at the margins. Apothecia pinkish-brown and often crowded.

Cortex C + r.

Habitat. Locally common on acid soil and peat in rock crevices, mainly in coastal areas.

L. wallrothii x6

CORTICOLOUS

L. cinnabarina [Protoblastenia cinnabarina] Thallus grey, thin but continuous, smooth or scurfy. Dotted with small, yellowish-buff, or greenish-grey sunken and clearly deliniated oval soralia. Normally sterile but when fertile the apothecia are small with a very dark red discs.

Soralia P + r. (It can be confused with *Haematomma elatinum* but that has a K + y cortex, with yellow-green, more irregular raised soralia).

Habitat. An old forest species where it is not rare in suitable habitats.

L. cinnabarina x10

L. quernea [Protoblastenia quernea]

Thallus ochre to yellow-grey consisting of very fine farinose soralia. The thallus is frequently surrounded by a grey prothallus. Usually infertile or with numerous small red-brown apothecia which darken with age and often look almost as if they are melting.

C + o. When infertile it may be confused with *Lecanora expallens* but this has coarser, less buff, more green-yellow soralia.

Habitat. Frequent on well-lit trees especially in 'old forests'.

L. quernea x8

THALLUS SQUAMULOSE
Section *Psora*
(see also *L. wallrothii* and *T. coarctata*)

L. scalaris [Hypocenomyce scalaris]

Thallus light grey-brown when dry becoming green-brown when wet, consisting of small convex almost fluted squamules to about 1 mm long and overlapping, the free end is turned upwards and covered with very fine soredia. Apothecia are rare with small, black, pruinose discs.

C + r.

Habitat. Common on fences and burnt wood, also found on acid-barked trees and brick walls. The rare but similar and more northern *L. friesii* is usually fertile with almost gyrose discs and is C−.

L. scalaris x18

L. decipiens [Psora decipiens] Thallus of pale pink or sometimes brown squamules with conspicuous white pruinose margins, often scattered over the substrate and circular or contorted. Apothecia up to 1 mm, black and convex with a lighter margin that becomes excluded. The apothecia are usually only one per squamule and situated towards the margin. K + mauve.

Habitat. A distinctive species of base-rich soils in the Scottish Highlands, but is also found on calcareous soils in Breckland and elsewhere.

L. decipiens x3

L. lurida [Psora lurida] Thallus green to coffee or dark chesnut – brown, the undersurface is often dark. Squamulose, imbricate, convex and contorted, often forming a thick crust. Apothecia up to about 1 mm, crowded, black or dark brown with the margins becoming excluded. Often confused with

Dermatocarpon hepaticum which has immersed perithecia. Habitat. Frequent in humus filled crevices in hard limestone or on calcareous soils.

L. lurida x6

LECIDELLA This genus is superficially like *Lecidea* but differs in that:
The paraphyses are branched and lax in K solution.
The hymenium reacts K + blue-green.
The asci react to iodine on the tholus.

L. elaeochroma x2500

1. Corticolous. Thallus yellow-grey to yellow-green, sometimes sorediate. C + o ....**L. elaeochroma**
    Saxicolous 2
2. Soralia delimited, yellow-green to green. Thallus greenish-grey C + o ....**L. scabra**
    Not sorediate. Thallus buff to yellow-grey. C + /–.........3
3. Thallus warted or granulose. Maritime siliceous rock. C + o
    ....**L. subincongrua**
    Thallus areolate or evanescent. Mainly calcareous, not strictly maritime C – ....**L. stigmatea**

CORTICOLOUS

Lecidella elaeochroma (Lecidea limitata)
Thallus yellow-grey to grey, slightly granular and usually shiny, often limited by a black prothallus and forming extensive mosaics. Usually fertile with black apothecia that are concave with a smooth black margin. It may be confused with *Catillaria lightfootii* which is sorediate, C- and has one septate spores.

Cortex C + o (in most cases).
Habitat. Very common on trees and fences.
The form *soralifera* has yellow or green farinose soralia scattered over the surface (apothecia are also normally present). Found mainly in the west.

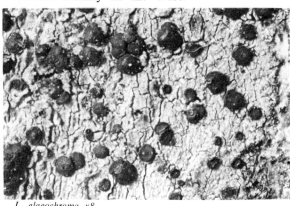

L. elaeochroma x8

form *soralifera*

SAXICOLOUS

L. subincongrua (Lecidea subincongrua)
Thallus buff to yellow-grey or greenish-yellow, thick usually very granulose, but may be almost areolate and warted, limited by a black prothallus. Apothecia appear almost innate becoming more sessile and convex with excluded margins. Disc brown to black.
Cortex C + o.
Habitat. Common on well-lit, hard, siliceous, maritime rocks.

L. subincongrua x10

L. scabra (Lecidea scabra) Thallus greenish-grey, granular and rough with delimited areas of pale yellow-green or green soralia which may become confluent. Apothecia rare, with slightly convex, black discs.
Cortex C + o.
Habitat. Common on hard, siliceous rocks and walls.

L. scabra x6

L. stigmatea (Lecidea stigmatea) Thallus pale green-grey or whitish, thick, areolate or almost evanescent.

Apothecia sessile, up to about 1mm across. Discs becoming convex, very dark brown or black.

Habitat. Common on calcareous rocks, asbestos or mortar. The thinner thallus is usually found when it is growing on siliceous substrates. May be confused with *Protoblastenia monticola* which has a red-brown hypothecium.

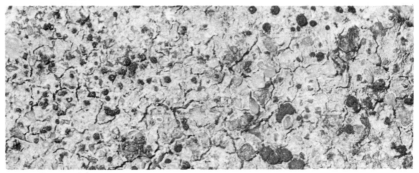

L. stigmatea x8

LEPRARIA Thallus leprose and consisting of a network of fungal hyphae with the phycobiont scattered amongst them. Some species do, however, have an almost lobate margin to the thallus. Fruiting bodies unknown.

1. Thallus yellow to emerald-green 2
    Thallus white, grey or blue-green..................................4
2. Thallus in tree crevices or on siliceous rocks K −........3
    Thallus on calcareous rocks. K + crimson.........**Leproplaca**
3. Emerald-green, on siliceous rocks in Scotland..**L. chlorina**
    Bright golden −yellow, in tree cracks...........**L. candelaris**
4. Grey to green-grey. Margins not subsquamulose. Very common ....**L. incana**
    Margin of thallus subsquamulose....................................5
5. Thallus yellow-white to pale green, shaded rocks and moss
    ....**L. membranacea**
    Thallus pure white to pale grey....................................6

6. Thallus soft, thick, on hard shaded calcareous rock ....**L. crassissima**
   Thallus scattered or small rosettes on siliceous rock or soil..7
7. P + r. Small neat rosettes on upland rocks........**L. zonata**
   P −. Irregular granules on peaty soil or mosses, rarely rocks, only found at high altitudes.................**L. neglecta**

Lepraria incana Thallus pale grey to green-grey, thick and may cover large areas.

Habitat. Very common on shaded rocks, trees and mosses. It even grows on trees near the centre of cities where it may be separated from the ubiquitous alga *Desmococcus* by its more grey less yellow-green colouration.

L. incana x3

L. neglecta Thallus light grey, coarsely granular and scattered or thick with a subsquamulose margin (can be confused with *L. zonata*).

Habitat. Rare, growing over mosses and on peaty soil, sometimes on siliceous rocks.

L. neglecta x5

L. zonata Thallus grey, granular and forming neat, rather circular patches with subsquamulose margins.
K + fy, P + r.
Habitat. Rare but locally common on siliceous rocks in the southern Pennines and also elsewhere. There is some doubt over the status of this species in Britain.

L. zonata x8

L. crassissima Thallus white or very pale grey, soft and thick forming delimited patches which are fluffy in the centre and weakly lobed at the margin.
Habitat. Locally abundant on shaded hard calcareous rocks (e.g. cave entrances).

L. crassissima x1

L. membranacea Thallus yellow-white to very pale green, thick, finely granular and forming roughly circular patches. Margins pale and slightly lobed.
Habitat. Not rare on dry shaded rocks especially on calcareous substrates, also over mosses on shaded deciduous trees.

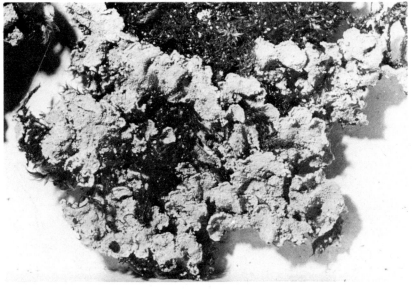

L. membranacea x10

L. candelaris Thallus bright golden-yellow, thin and of powdery granules or forming a matt crust.

K−.

Habitat. Common in dry shaded crevices on rough barked deciduous trees, especially oak. Often found with *Calicium viride*, *Lecanactis abietina* and *Chaenotheca ferruginea*.

L. candelaris x20

L. chlorina Thallus lemon-yellow, to almost emerald when fresh, thick and granular.

K −.

Habitat. A rather rare but distinctive species found in dry crevices of hard siliceous rocks in the eastern Highlands of Scotland.

L. chlorina x7

LEPROCAULON see STEREOCAULON

LEPROPLACA Separated from the genus *Lepraria* by the presence of a cortex and the K + purple reaction due to parietin.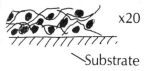

x20

↘Substrate

Thallus deep mustard – yellow throughout. Not lobate
.... **L. chrysodeta**
Thallus mustard to green-yellow, white medulla. Lobate at margin ....**L. xantholyta**

Leproplaca chrysodeta Thallus deep mustard, granulose, not lobate at the margins.
K + p.
Habitat. Common in the dry crevices of hard calcareous rocks and walls.

L. chrysodeta x10

L. xantholyta Thallus mustard-yellow to green-yellow with a white medulla and delimited by a white prothallus lobate at the margins.
K + p.
Habitat. Frequent in dry crevices of hard calcareous rocks.

L. xantholyta x5

LEPTOGIUM Thallus foliose, homoiomerous but unlike *Collema* the apical cells of the hyphae near the surface almost form a cortical layer. Apothecia lecanorine, spores 3-5 septate or muriform, chemical reactions are negative. Many species are difficult to separate.

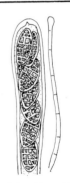

L. lichenoides x350

1. Isidiate...2
   Lacking isidia 3
2. Lobes forming a dense mat 3–5mm high, striated, margins with digitate isidia ....**L. lichenoides**
   Lobes to 2cm across, less erect, with flat laminal isidia ....**L. cyanescens**
3. Lobes wrinkled when dry, erect, green-brown. Usually fertile ....**L. sinuatum**
   Lobes not wrinkled when dry, less erect, green-grey to blue-grey. Rarely fertile ....**L. tremelloides**

Leptogium lichenoides Thallus dark brown or grey-brown, usually consisting of a dense mat of more or less erect lobes about 3-5mm high. Each lobe is thin and striate when dry, the margins normally bearing digitate isidia. Usually infertile. Apothecia when present with chestnut-brown discs with a lighter margin. Spores persistently muriform.

Habitat. Common on mosses on trees or calcareous rocks or with mosses on damp calcareous soils.

L lichenoides x4

L. tremelloides [L. britannicum] Thallus translucent dark green-grey when wet, pale blue-grey when dry. The lobes are thin and papery with a smooth edge and not wrinkled when dry. The lobes are frequently almost circular and up to 2cm across. It often forms extensive patches and is rarely fertile. Apothecia with

reddish-brown discs. Spores 3 septate becoming muriform. Habitat. Common in western Ireland and Scotland but occasionally found in the south-west and west of Britain amongst mosses on damp rocks or calcareous soils, mostly in maritime areas.

L. tremelloides x6

L. cyanescens Similar to the previous species but having larger, less erect lobes bearing flat laminal isidia that become dense towards the centre of the thallus. It forms colonies up to about 5cm across. Apothecia very rare.

Habitat. Rare in the west, amongst mosses on trees and rocks in maritime regions.

L. cyanescens x5

L. sinuatum Thallus green-brown to brown, erect, wrinkled, either with entire margins or regularly lacerate, not isidiate. Usually abundantly fertile. Apothecia up to 1.5mm diam. with red-brown to brown discs. Spores muriform.
Habitat. Rather rare amongst mosses on trees and rocks, calcareous soils and mortar.

8

L. sinuatum x8

LICHINA Thallus fruticose, dark brown to black. The fungal hyphae usually form a central core and also a cortical layer one or two cells thick. Apothecia apical. Spores simple, 8 per ascus. Saxicolous and maritime. There are only two British species, although others are being investigated. They look rather like small brown seaweeds.

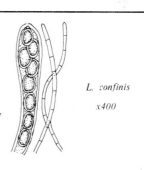

L. confinis

x400

Thallus to 1cm high, lobes flattened. Below high-water mark. ....**L. pygmaea**
Thallus less than 5mm high. Lobes more or less terete. Usually around high-water mark. ....**L. confinis**

Lichina pygmaea Thallus matt dark brown to black, sometimes with some yellow-brown branches, flattened except towards the tips which may be terete. It forms extensive mats up to about 1cm high. Apothecia spherical on the tips of the branches.
Habitat. Common on rocks on exposed shores in the upper part of the tidal region below h.w.m.

L. pygmaea x6

L. confinis Thallus dark brown to black, matt, much smaller than the previous species (less than 5mm high), and more richly branched, terete, forming a short dense mat which often originates from sheltered crevices. Apothecia spherical and found on the tips of the branches.
Habitat. Very common on rocks on sheltered shores around h.w.m. (above *L. pygmaea*).

L. confinis x7

LOBARIA Thallus foliose, lower surface tomentose. Apothecia lecanorine. Spores colourless or brown, septate. These large species flourish in unpolluted regions and are therefore commonest on the western side of Britain. They differ from *Sticta* species by the absence of cyphellae on the undersurface.

L. pulmonaria x600

1. Thallus sorediate, isidiate or with black coralloid outgrowths 3
   Thallus lacking soralia, isidia or black outgrowths 2
2. Thallus silver-grey to pale buff, little changed when wet, sometimes wrinkled. Med. KC + red ....**L. amplissima**
   Thallus bright green when wet, to grey-brown, lobes more or less smooth. Med. KC- ....**L. laetevirens**
3. Thallus silver-grey with black coralloid outgrowths ....**L. amplissima**
   Thallus blue-grey, khaki, or green, sorediate or isidiate..4
4. Lobes ridged, bright green or khaki, isidia or soralia on ridges ....**L. pulmonaria**
   Lobes smooth, blue-grey to yellow-grey, globose soralia or isidia (cephalodia) towards the lobe tips .....**L. scrobiculata**

147

Lobaria pulmonaria Thallus bright clear green when wet, becoming khaki to green-grey when dry. Upper surface shiny, wrinkled and pustulate. Lower surface light tan with a darker tomentum which becomes rubbed off on the raised parts of the thallus. The lobes are up to about 20cm long, and the ends are often incised. Soralia, which become isidiate, form along the ridges on the upper surface. Usually infertile. Apothecia found mainly on the margins of the lobes, red-brown, often with a thin margin. Spores 1-3 septate.

This species used to be common and was collected in large quantities as "lungwort" and due to its lung-like appearance was sold as a cure for lung diseases. The other members of the Stictaceae have either little smell or an unpleasant fishy one. *L. pulmonaria* is, however, an exception and after processing is used in perfume manufacture. It has even been used instead of hops for beer making.

Medulla K + y to r,P + o to r.

Habitat. Frequent in the west on deciduous trees and is "an old forest species". Sometimes on mossy rocks and occasionally on heather stems. It is found throughout Britain, but is now rare on the eastern side.

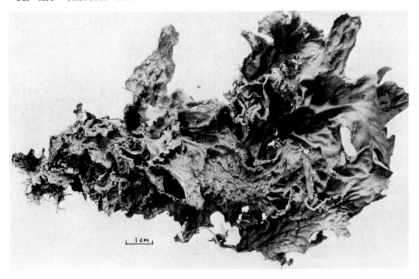

L. pulmonaria x0.8

L. laetevirens Thallus green when wet, green-grey to grey-brown when dry. Undersurface almost white with a brown tomentum. Lobes short, narrow and unridged (looking like a *Parmelia* species), imbricate and more adpressed than the previous species, the inner lobes incised and contorted, the marginal lobes rounded and smooth. No soralia. Usually with abundant apothecia which, when young, appear as a volcano-like swelling which opens out to form a fruit with a brown disc and warted margin. Spore colourless becoming brown when mature. Spores persistently 1 septate.

Reactions negative.

Habitat. As *L. pulmonaria*.

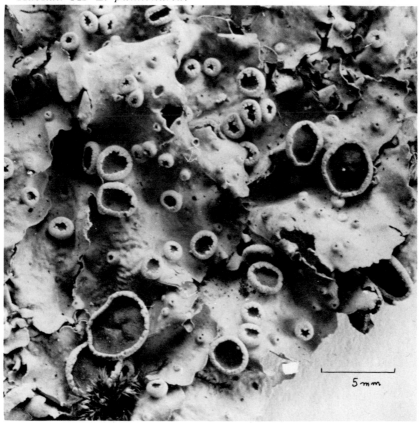

L. laetevirens x4

L. amplissima Thallus pale silvery-grey when wet, becoming more brownish when dry. Undersurface pale brown tomentose. Lobes adpressed, large, smooth towards the inscised tips, wrinkled in the centre of the thallus. Up to 25cm across. Large mature specimens sometimes have clusters of brown-black

coralloid outgrowths containing a blue-green alga. These probably assist the plant with fixing atmospheric nitrogen and are an example where the form of the lichen is modified when the phycobiont is changed. Usually found sterile. Apothecia red-brown. Spores 1-3 septate.

Medulla KC + r.

Habitat. As *L. pulmonaria* but much rarer; now only frequent in north-west Scotland, although it is still present in south-west England and the Lake District.

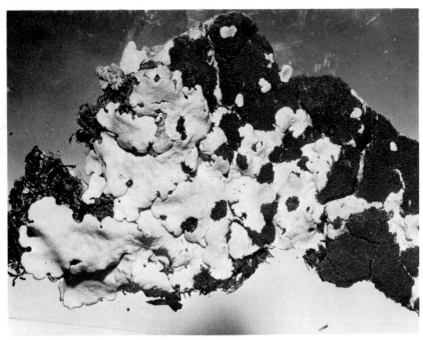

L. amplissima ×2

L. scrobiculata Thallus blue-grey when wet, looking yellowish when dry. Lobes up to about 15cm long, ridged, attached only towards the centre. Undersurface tomentose brown-black in the centre and pale tan at the margin, with small white areas which look like cyphellae and may cause confusion with *Sticta* species.

Coarse soralia or isidia form dark, almost globose areas mainly on the ridges near the lobe tips. Apothecia are rare, with a red-brown disc. Spores colourless, becoming brown, 1-3 septate. Medulla K + y, KC + r, P + o.

Habitat. As *L. pulmonaria* but much rarer, except in north-west Scotland, where it is frequent.

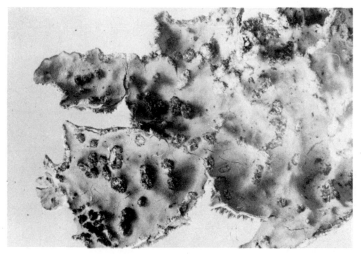

L. scrobiculata x5

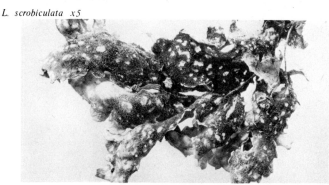

L. scrobiculata (undersurface) x1.5

MENEGAZZIA Closely related to the genus *Hypogymnia,* it has the same inflated foliose thallus but differs in the upper surface being perforated with small holes. Apothecia lecanorine. Spores colourless, simple. There is only one British species.

M. terebrata x6

Menegazzia terebrata Thallus grey, smooth, adpressed and inflated. Upper surface perforated by small holes which are often sorediate, or sometimes globose soralia on short stalks are found. The lower surface is wrinkled and fixed to the substrate by suckers. Apothecia have not been found on the British species.

Cortex K + y. Medulla K + y, P + o.

Habitat. Rare on trees, heather stems and rocks in the West. It is an "old forest" species.

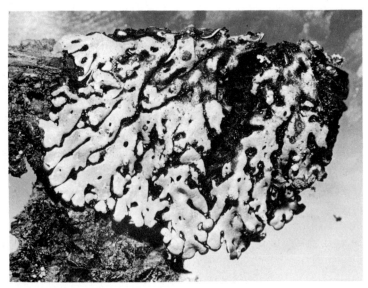

M. terebrata x4

MYCOBLASTUS Thallus crustose, granular, medulla sometimes with red areas. Apothecia lecideine. Spores colourless, simple, very large and only 1 to 3 in each ascus. Each spore contains many nuclei.

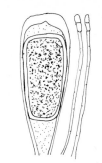

Mycoblastus sanguinarius Thallus grey, thick, either granular or warted, or thin when growing over mosses. Medulla red under apothecia and often showing red through the cortex elsewhere. Usually fertile. Apothecia up to 3mm diam. Discs black, becoming strongly convex, sometimes innate. Spores large, usually one, but up to 3 per ascus. Cortex K + y.

M. sanguinarius x200

Habitat. Common in upland areas on hard siliceous rocks or over mosses on deciduous trees.

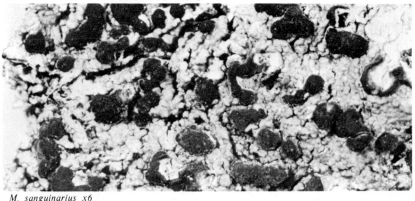

M. sanguinarius x6

NEPHROMA The generic name is derived from the Greek for kidney. Thallus foliose. Apothecia lecideine and borne on the undersurface of the lobe ends. This, together with the bare lower surface, separates this genus from *Peltigera* and *Solorina*. Spores at first colourless but becoming darker, 1-3 septate, 8 per ascus.

N. laevigatum x400

153

Nephroma laevigatum Thallus brown-grey, shining, the lobes short and often much incised. Undersurface buff, bare and wrinkled. Medulla pale yellow.Usually fertile. Apothecia found on the lower surface of the lobe tip. These lobes are often longer than the infertile lobes and curved back to show

the apothecia. Smaller apothecia have distinct margins and there may be several on one lobe. Some apothecia may be up to 1 cm or more across and wider than the lobe on which they grow. Spores 3 septate.

Medulla K + o to r. A very rare species *N. bellum* is K − and has a white medulla. *N. parile* also has a white medulla and is most commonly found in the west. It is rarely fertile and has abundant blue-grey soralia along the margins and sometimes on the surface of the lobes.

Habitat. Locally abundant in the west on mossy trees, walls and rocks. An "old forest" species.

N. laevigatum x5

NORMANDINA Thallus of small squamules that become sorediate. Fruiting bodies are unknown and it is just possible that this is a basidiomycete. There is only one species in the genus.

Sphaerulina chlorococca x1000

Normandina pulchella Thallus pale green-grey or pruinose, circular with raised margins or oystershell-shaped squamules. The squamules are usually less than 1mm wide but may be up to 5mm. They become sorediate around the raised margin and the soredia may spread to cover the whole of the thallus. The perithecia which are sometimes found on the thallus are now known to belong to a parasitic fungus growing on the thallus *(Sphaerulina chlorococca).*

Habitat. Common on mosses on trees or rocks, especially in light shade. Sometimes found growing on other lichens in very damp situations.

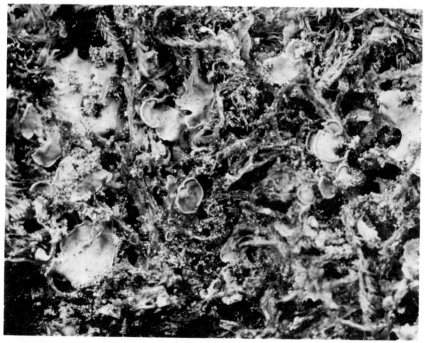

N. pulchella x8

OCHROLECHIA Thallus crustose and warted. Apothecia lecanorine. Spores colourless, simple, very large, two or more per ascus. This genus is very closely related to *Pertusaria*. Up to the end of the last century they were of importance for dyeing and were collected in large quantities for this purpose.

O. parella x200

1. Isidiate or sorediate..2
   Lacking isidia or soralia...6
2. Isidiate..3
   Sorediate 4
3. Isidia delicate and massed. C + r.....................**O. yasudae**
   Isidia coarse. C −...**O. turneri**
4. Soralia yellow or yellowish...5
   Soralia from broken down isidia, coarse, grey or greenish-grey .... **O. yasudae**
5. Thallus pale grey or yellowish-grey, warted crust. C + o ....**O. androgyna**
   Thallus greenish-grey, thin. C + o ....**O. inversa**
6. Thallus white to pale grey, coarsely granular. Cortex and disc C + rose..**O. tartarea**
   Thallus fawn to grey, not coarsely granular, white prothallus. Cortex C −, disc KC + r.................**O. parella**

Ochrolechia parella Thallus grey to buff-grey with a white prothallus. It forms large patches up to 20 cms across. Thick and warted in the centre, but sometimes smooth when found on trees. There are no soralia present. Usually abundantly fertile. Apothecia 2-3mm diam, but may be as much as 5mm, margins thick and rough. Discs flesh to pink. When on rocks the disc is usually covered in a thick white, often cracked, pruina that almost

appears papillose. It was used for dyeing and may have been the source of the purple dye "perelle".

Cortex C −, Discs KC + r.

Habitat. Very common on hard, smooth siliceous rocks and walls, especially slates and schists, mainly in upland and maritime regions. It is also found on trees.

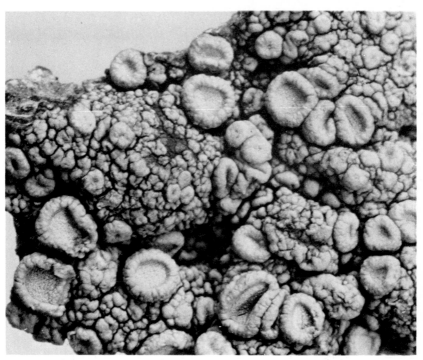

O. parella x6.

O. tartarea Thallus yellowish-grey or creamy, large, of compacted convex granules or warted. No soralia. Apothecia have a thick, notched, margin and are 3-6 mm diam, but may be up to 1cm. Disc flesh pink to brown, rough. This species was used to produce a dye called "cudbear". This process was  patented in 1758 and is believed to be derived from Cuthbert, the Christian name of the inventor.

Cortex and disc C + rose.

Habitat. Common on trees, rocks and mosses in areas with a very high rainfall.

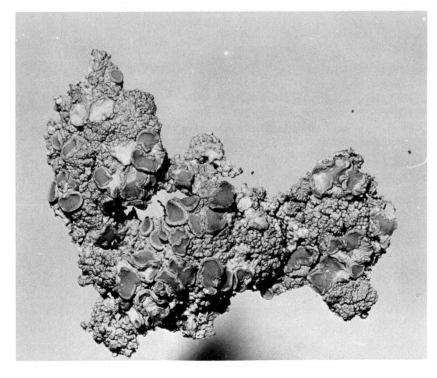

O. tartarea x2

O. androgyna Thallus grey or yellowish-grey forming a thick warted crust often with a distinct white prothallus. Yellowish-grey soralia up to several millimetres across are found scattered over the surface, sometimes becoming confluent. Usually infertile except in the south-west and the western Highlands

of Scotland where it may be abundantly fertile. Apothecia up to 1cm diam. Disc-flesh coloured with a pale, smooth, entire margin. Like the preceding species it was used in the production of cudbear.

Cortex and soralia C + red.

Habitat. Widespread on acid-barked trees and siliceous rocks, or growing over mosses. It becomes rarer in the south and east.

O. androgyna x6

O. yasudae Thallus grey to green-grey, covered with delicate, short, massed isidia that may break down and become sorediate in old specimens. Apothecia rare, only found in unpolluted areas in the west. Discs pink, often pruinose and usually with an isidiate margin. Separated by the C + red reaction from the more coarsely isidiate *O. turneri*.

Habitat. Frequent on nutrient-rich rough-barked deciduous trees.

O. yasudae x12

O. inversa Thallus greenish-grey with yellow soralia that become confluent. Not known fertile in Britain.

Thallus and soralia C + orange to red.

Habitat. On acidic bark, particularly in the south and west, where it is widely distributed but rarely abundant.

O. inversa x6

OPEGRAPHA Thallus crustose. Phycobiont *Trentepohlia*. Ascocarps carbonaceous lirellae. Spores colourless, fusiform, or clavate · 3 + septate, 8 per ascus. Due to the soft nature of the hyphae, there are very few fossil lichens. However, one of the earliest records of lichens is probably an *Opegrapha* species that was found in Mesozoic chalk.

O. saxatilis x200

4. Thallus glaucous white, lirellae short, pruinose, on old dry oaks...**O. lyncea**
   Thallus brown to grey or evanescent, sometimes pruinose. Mainly on ash or elm..................................**O. lichenoides**
5. Thallus grey, lirellae numerous often crowded in the centre of the thallus..**O. atra**
   Thallus brown, lirellae scattered ....**O. vulgata**
6. Sorediate, not with white pruinose pycnidia..................7
   Thallus pinkish-grey, not sorediate but with papilla-like, white, pruinose pycnidia ....**O. vermicellifera**
7. Thallus red-brown, soralia orange..................**O. gyrocarpa**
   Thallus greenish-grey, soralia yellowish-green.**O. corticola**
8. No soralia. Thallus white to brown grey......................9
   Orange soralia. Thallus reddish-brown...........**O. gyrocarpa**
9. Spores 4–5 septate and clavate. Thallus pale grey, slightly purple, dark prothallus.............................. **O. cesareensis**
   Spores 3 septate, not clavate. Thallus colour various or endolithic 10
10. Thallus endolithic or pale pink leprose, lirellae stellate, shaded limestone...**O. calcarea**
    Thallus grey to dark brown or endolithic, lirellae in heaps, siliceous or calcareous substrates 11
11. Thallus light to dark brown, scurfy or endolithic, lirellae unbranched, scattered or in heaps...................**O. saxatilis**
    Thallus brownish-grey, thin or endolithic, lirellae contorted and heaped in gyrose piles or short and round**O. confluens**

CORTICOLOUS
(See also *O. gyrocarpa*)

Opegrapha atra Thallus light grey or white, delimited or sometimes almost evanescent. Lirellae short (up to about 2mm), often densely crowded in the centre of the thallus. Some forms can resemble *Graphis scripta* but the smaller, more prominent lirellae and the 3 septate spores separate the species.

Habitat. This is the commonest of the British *Opegrapha* species and the most easily recognised. It is found on trees, especially those lightly shaded with smooth bark, also on twigs and rarely on fences.

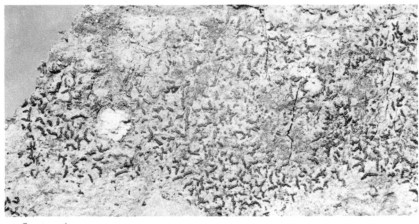

O. atra x6

O. vulgata Thallus brown or light brown, thin, with more separated lirellae than the previous species. The lirellae are slender and may be straight, curved or sometimes stellate. Black dot-like pycnidia are often scattered amongst the lirellae. Spores 4-8 septate, but mainly 6 septate.

Habitat. Very common on shaded smooth-barked trees.

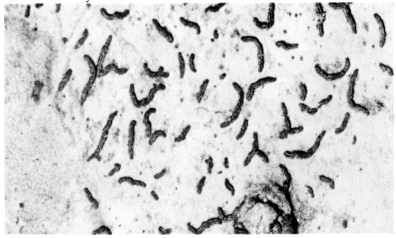

O. vulgata x12

O. lyncea Thallus glaucous white to white, thicker than the other species of *Opegrapha* and forming a bright patch on the substrate. Lirellae short and broad and covered with a pale grey pruina. Spores mainly 6-7 septate.

Habitat. Locally frequent in the south and east in unpolluted areas. Almost entirely restricted to dry recesses and bough underhangs on ancient oak trees.

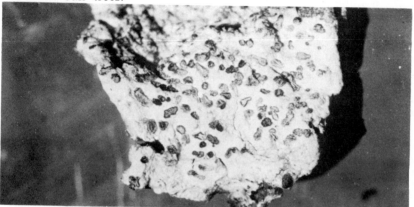

O. lyncea x10

O. lichenoides Thallus brown to grey-brown or evanescent. Lirellae less than 1mm long and opening widely, often to exclude the margin and expose the grey pruinose disc. Spores mainly 5 septate, but may be 4-8 septate.

Habitat. Common and widespread on nutrient-rich rough bark, especially elm and ash.

O. lichenoides x6

O. vermicellifera Thallus light grey. Usually sterile when it can be recognised by the small (about 0.25mm) papilla-like pycnidia which are covered in a white pruina. Lirellae slender, with a pruinose more open disc than *O. vulgata*. Spores 5 septate.

The C − reaction of the pycnidial pruina separates it from superficially similar sterile *Lecanactis abietina* which has C + red pycnidial pruina.

Habitat. Frequent in dry recesses on shaded trees, especially elm. When on oak and also spreading on to ivy, stones, etc., it is usually the superficially similar *Lecanactis subabietina*.

O. vermicellifera x12

SAXICOLOUS

O. calcarea Thallus usually endolithic or pale pink and may be slightly leprose. Lirellae small (1-2mm long), stellate and black. Spores 3 septate.

Habitat. Widespread on shaded limestone.

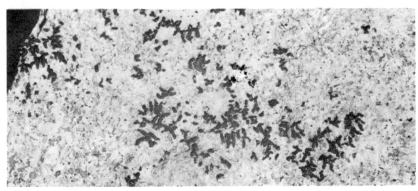

O. calcarea x6

O. saxatilis Thallus light to dark brown, rough and scurfy, or may be endolithic (especially on calcareous rocks). Lirellae fairly large, unbranched and sometimes piled up in heaps. Spores 3 septate. Habitat. Frequent on both siliceous and calcareous substrates.

O. saxatilis x6

O. confluens Thallus light grey to brown-grey, thin or arachnoid or evanescent, lacking a prothallus. Lirellae mainly central, some short and almost round, but mainly long and contorted and gathered into heaps. Spores 3 septate. Habitat. Widespread and locally abundant on siliceous rocks, rarely on calcareous rock; especially common in maritime regions in the north and west.

O. confluens x6

O. cesareensis Thallus white or light grey, often slightly purple, thin and smooth or thicker and cracked, limited by a dark prothallus. Lirellae mainly short and very prominent. Spores 4-5 septate, distinctly clavate.

Habitat. Not infrequent in the West on shaded or under overhanging siliceous rocks.

O. cesareensis x10

O. gyrocarpa Thallus red-brown, fairly thick with a leprose surface. Yellow to orange soralia, which may become confluent, are dotted over the surface. Lirellae if present, fairly short and contorted so as to appear gyrose. Spores 3 septate.

C + r.

Habitat. Frequent in shaded recesses and underhangs of siliceous rocks. A very similar species *O. corticola* has a grey thallus and is found on trees in the extreme south of England.

O. gyrocarpa x4

PACHYPHIALE Thallus crustose. Apothecia lecideine. Spores 8 or more per ascus, colourless, multiseptate.

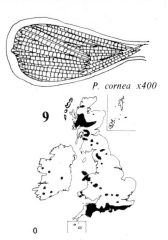

P. cornea x400

Pachyphiale cornea Thallus thin, light buff-grey. Apothecia about 0.5mm across, light buff when young becoming dark, translucent reddish-brown. Margin pronounced and entire giving it the appearance of a very small wine-gum. Habitat. Locally abundant on rough-barked deciduous trees in established woodlands.

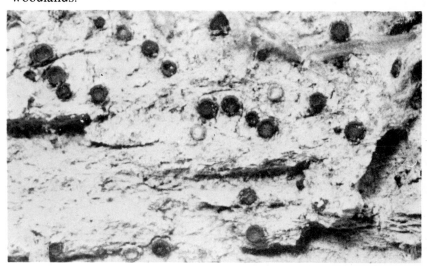

P. cornea x12

PANNARIA Thallus squamulose. Undersurface a dark felted hypothallus. Apothecia lecanorine. Spores simple, colourless, 8 per ascus. They may be separated from the similar *Parmeliella* species by the presence of the thalline margin to the apothecia. There are a number of British species, but most are rare.

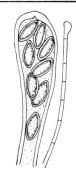

P. rubiginosa x400

Thallus, a rosette of imbricate squamules. No soralia.......
.... **P. rubiginosa**
Thallus of elongate, separate squamules. Margins soreditate
or ísidiate (found in other rare species) ....**P. pityrea**

Pannaria rubiginosa Thallus bluish-grey
to brown-grey, forming rosettes of
imbricate squamules, 1-4mm wide,
much incised and with a whiter margin.
Undersurface tomentose grey to black.
Usually fertile. Apothecia up to 2mm
across with a crenulate margin. Disc
chestnut-red, paler when young, but
becoming darker red when wet.

Habitat. An oceanic species now only commonly encountered in
the extreme west of Scotland and Ireland, usually overgrowing
mosses on trees and rocks.

P. rubiginosa x3.5

P. pityrea [P. conoplea] Thallus blue-grey or yellowish-grey, consisting of long separate squamules (not rosettes), up to about 6mm long, imbricate, adpressed and deeply incised, often pruinose. Soralia, which may be coarse and isidia-like are formed on the margins and may spread over the surface to form a complete crust. Undersurface tomentose, grey-brown to black. Rarely fertile. Apothecia with chestnut discs and sorediate margins.

Habitat. Similar to *P. rubiginosa* but less strongly oceanic, but commonest in the extreme west. It is an "old forest" indicator species.

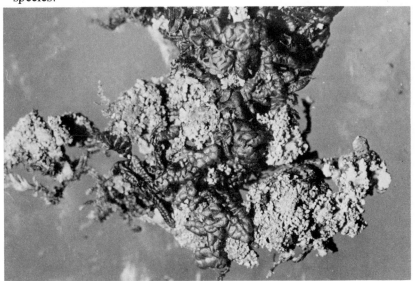

P. pityrea x5

PARMELIA Thallus foliose, lobate. Apothecia lecanorine, sessile or stalked. Spores simple, colourless, 2-8 per ascus. This is a large genus of world-wide distribution, some species of which were important sources of dyes. The chemical reactions are very useful in the identification of species.

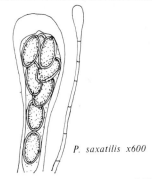

P. saxatilis x600

169

1. Thallus grey or green-grey 2
   Thallus green-brown to dark metallic brown; or yellow-green to yellow-grey 16
2. Thallus sorediate or isidiate. Medulla C + r or − 3
   Thallus lacking soredia or isidia. Medulla C + r 15
3. Thallus sorediate 4
   Thallus isidiate 12
4. Medulla C + red 5
   Medulla C − 8
5. Soralia mainly marginal or apical. Thallus lacking pseudocyphellae 6
   Soralia laminal and punctiform, thallus with white dot-like pseudocyphellae 7
6. Thallus light grey, lobe ascending, bent back at the lips. Soralia creamy yellow-grey .... **P. revoluta**
   Thallus mid-grey, lobes adpressed, soralia with blue-black speckles .... **P. britannica**
7. Undersurface light brown .... **P. subrudecta**
   Undersurface black .... **P. borreri**
8. Thallus with white pseudocyphellae in dots and lines, often on ridges, or forming a net of fine white lines (x10 lens)..9
   Thallus without white pseudocyphellae 11
9. Thallus with fine net of white lines, often with black cilia on the margins. South and east .... **P. reticulata**
   Thallus with coarser, white pseudocyphellae. No cilia.10
10. Soralia not on ridges. Punctiform to confluent. Medulla P − .... **P. reddenda**
    Soralia on ridges. Linear to confluent. Medulla P + r. .... **P. sulcata**
11. Lobe tips rounded, undersurface dark brown becoming tan at margins. Rhizinae simple .... **P. perlata**
    Lobe tips truncated. Undersurface black. Rhizinae various but not simple .... **P. laevigata**
12. Thallus with white pseudocyphellae or black cilia. C − .13
    Thallus without pseudocyphellae or cilia. Medulla C + red 14
13. Pseudocyphellae, as white lines and dots. Grey to brown

coralloid isidia, growing from lines. No cilia....**P.saxatilis**
No pseudocyphellae. Laminal and marginal cilia. Scattered clumps of coralloid isidia ....**P. crinita**

14. Isidia mid-brown, coralloid. Mainly eastern ....**P. tiliacea**
Isidia dark brown to black, bun-shaped head. Westerly and southerly...**P. pastillifera**

15. Thallus grey with green tinge. Lobe ascending. Rhizinae branched. Not fertile. Trees and rocks.......**P. taylorensis**
Thallus whitish-grey, adpressed. Rhizinae simple. Mainly ıertile. Upper tree canopy...............................**P. quercina**

16. Thallus green-brown to dark metallic-brown 17
Thallus yellow-green to yellow-grey 29

17. Thallus isidiate, sorediate or with many small warts..18
Thallus without isidia, soredia or small warts.............24

18. Medulla C + red...19
Medulla C − 21

19. Thallus dark brown to black with dense coralloid isidia. On rocks....................................**P. glabratula** subsp. **fuliginosa**
Thallus green-brown, mainly on trees, rarely rocks 20

20. Thallus glossy, isidia coralloid, breaking off to leave white scars ....**P. glabratula**
Thallus often slightly matt. Isidia more granular and leaving pale yellow scars ....**P. subaurifera**

21. Thallus adpressed with numerous small volcano-like warts (x 10 lens). No isidia ....**P. exasperata**
Thallus with isidia not warts......................................22

22. Isidia simple, spoon − shaped. Undersurface pale ....**P. exasperatula**
Isidia not spoon-shaped. Undersurface black...............23

23. Lobes pale brown, convex, ridged. Isidia almost spherical and in groups ....**P. loxodes**
Lobes dark brown to black, adpressed, more or less smooth. Isidia flattened and scattered ....**P. verruculifera**

24. Medulla K + yellow to red 25
Medulla K − 26

25. Thallus brown with purple tinge, well difined reticulum of raised, pale − coloured lines. Mainly siliceous rocks. Widespread..**P. omphalodes**

Thallus leaden to greenish, no pale lines. Mainly on bark in the east..**P. acetabulum**

26. Thallus brown with a clear reticulum of pale lines ....**P. discordans**
Thallus chocolate to mid-brown with no, or only a very faint pale reticulum (x 10 lens)....................................27

27. Lobes less than 1mm wide, in dense overlapping tufts. Undersurface pale.......................................**P. laciniatula**
Lobes more than 1mm wide. Undersurface black in centre 28

28. Thallus chocolate-brown. Medulla KC −..............**P. pulla**
Thallus mid-brown. Medulla KC + red. Rare ....**P. delisei**

29. Lobes usually imbricate, with massed delicate coralloid isidia...**P. conspersa**
Thallus sorediate not isidiate..30

30. Thallus to 5cm across. Lobes to 2mm wide. Soralia farinose and globose 31
Thallus to 10cm across. Lobes wider (to about 1cm). Soralia coarse, rather granular 32

31. Lobes about 1mm wide. Thallus dark and granular in the centre. Soralia laminal. P + o.........................**P. mougeotii**
Lobes about 2mm wide. Curved under at tips. Soralia apical. P −...**P. incurva**

32. Medulla and soralia K + y ....**P. caperata**
Medulla and soralia K + r. Lobes more adpressed............
....**P. soredians**

Types of rhizinae

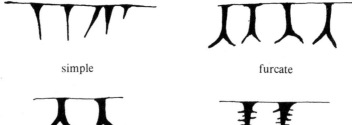

simple   furcate

dichotomous   squarrose

THALLUS GREY OR GREEN-GREY
Sorediate

Parmelia sulcata Thallus orbicular, grey to glaucous-white, consisting of overlapping ridged and sinuate lobes, normally covered with a faint white reticulum along which soralia develops, these may spread and cover the centre of the thallus. Undersurface very dark brown with black rhizinae. Usually infertile except in the north and west. Apothecia with a dark brown disc. Distinguished from *P. saxatilis* by the presence of soralia as opposed to isidia.

Medulla and soralia K + y to r, P + r.

Habitat. Very common on trees and rocks throughout Britain, especially in lowland areas.

P. sulcata x3

P. perlata Thallus light pearly grey, orbicular and up to 15cm across. Lobes smooth, up to 2cm across with ascending, incised and undulating margins which have delimited soralia on the lobe tips. Black cilia up to about 2mm long are sometimes found around the margin. Undersurface black in the  centre with simple rhizinae, tan-coloured towards the margins and almost devoid of rhizinae. It may be easily detached from the substrate. It has been used to produce a brown dye and a closely related species has been eaten in India in curry.
Cortex K + y, medulla K + y, P + o.

Habitat. Common in the south and west but becoming rarer northwards. Found on trees and rocks, it is very pollution sensitive.

P. perlata x0.6

P. laevigata Thallus light grey, large, orbicular. Lobes long and relatively narrow (up to 1cm wide), rather rectangular with square cut tips and curved axils. The lobe tips have delimited soralia. Undersurface black. It may be separated from *P. perlata* by the lobe shape, the black undersurface, and

the bifurcate or squarrose rhizinae. It is also P −.

Cortex K + y Medulla KC + o.

Habitat. Common in very high rainfall areas in the west, growing over mosses or trees or rocks. A similar but rare species *P. endochlora* has a yellow medulla and is found in coastal western Scotland.

P laevigata x2

P. britannica Thallus darker grey than the previous species, much smaller (lobes only 2-3mm wide) with a wrinkled surface. Lobe apices have dark speckled blue-black, granular soralia. Undersurface dark in the centre, tan at the margins. Rhizinae simple or dichotomous.

Cortex K + y, medulla C + r.

Habitat. Locally common on exposed, well-lit, coastal rocks in the west.

P. britannica x1.5

P. revoluta Thallus light grey, orbicular, up to 10cm across. Lobes short, incised and revolute. The margins have soralia especially near the apices. The soralia spread over the lobe and are not sharply delimited. Undersurface dark with short simple rhizinae towards the centre, tan and without rhizinae at the margins. It

may be separated from *P. laevigata* by the smaller size, the more rounded revolute lobes and the C + red reaction. It has lighter soralia than *P. britannica*.

Cortex K + y, Medulla C + r.

Habitat. Widespread, but rarely common on trees and rocks.

P. revoluta x5

P. reticulata Thallus glaucous grey, up to 15cm or more across, smooth with fine, white, areolate reticulations (visible with a hand lens). The lobes are ascending and then frequently turn down at the apices which are crenulate (more so in the centre than at the edges of the lobes). Soralia and black cilia are

usually present on the tips and margins of the lobes. Undersurface dark brown to black with simple rhizinae, slightly lighter towards the margin. Apothecia are very rare, brown with an entire margin.

Cortex K + y, Medulla K + y to r, C −, P −.

Habitat. Widespread but rarely abundant in low rainfall areas of the south and east on trees (rarely on moss-covered rocks).

P. reticulata x1

P. reddenda Thallus grey, lobes less than 1cm wide. The upper surface has white pseudocyphellae, which may break out into granular soralia that sometimes spread over the surface of the lobes. Undersurface black with a lighter margin.

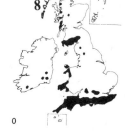

Cortex K + y, Medulla and soralia C −.

Habitat. An "old forest" species that is fairly rare in the south on trees and moss-covered rocks.

P. reddenda x2

P. subrudecta Thallus grey, orbicular with smooth or nearly smooth rounded lobes, sprinkled with delimited farinose soralia which erupt from the white pseudocyphallae and along the margins of the lobes. Undersurface light brown with simple rhizinae.

Cortex K + y, Medulla C + r, KC + r, Soralia C + r.

Habitat. Common, but becoming rarer in the north . Found on trees and moss on rocks.

P. subrudecta x2

P. borreri Very similar in appearance to *P. subrudecta* except for the black undersurface. It may be separated from *P. reddenda* by the C + r reaction.

Cortex K + y, Soralia C + r, P + y.

Habitat. Not common, but overlooked for *P. subrudecta*. Found mainly in the south on trees and moss-covered rocks.

P. borreri x4

Isidiate

P. saxatilis Thallus pale grey to green-grey in shade. Lobes rather narrow, ridged, widening slightly at the tips. Pseudocyphellae form a reticulum of white lines in the upper cortex (see *P. sulcata* and *P. omphalodes*). Grey-brown isidia are formed on the reticulum and become confluent.  Undersurface very dark brown, lighter at the margins. The undersurface out to the margin is covered in simple or bifurcate rhizinae. Apothecia rather rare, up to about 1cm across. Disc dark red-brown, margins thin and frequently isidiate or crenulate.

Cortex K + y, P + y, Medulla K + y − r, P + o.

Habitat. Very common throughout Britain on trees, stone walls and rocks. Specimens growing on human bones used to be considered to have medicinal properties. The most prized was said to grow on the skull of a hanged man (although this may have been a moss). This species was also much used to produce a reddish-brown dye.

P. saxatilis x3

P. tiliacea Thallus blue-grey, lobes rounded and slightly erect. Undersurface black with simple rhizinae in the centre, light brown and almost without rhizinae at the margin. The lobes bear simple or branched coralloid isidia which have brown tips. These isidia may spread to cover the centre of the thallus.

Apothecia very rare in Britain with red-brown discs, margins often isidiate, rhizinae are frequently found on the lower surface of the apothecia.

Cortex K + y, Medulla C + r.

Habitat. Widespread, but not common, mainly in the eastern half of Britain. Found on trees and rocks.

P. tiliacea x4

P. pastillifera Very similar to the previous species but with a lighter more blue-grey thallus, more adpressed. The isidia expand to form very dark brown bun-shaped heads several times wider than the stalks. These are usually more scattered and less crowded than in *P. tiliacea*. Apothecia very rare in Britain, similar in form to the previous species.

Cortex K + y, Medulla C + r.

Habitat. Frequent in the damper west and south of Britain. Found on trees and rocks.

P. pastillifera x5

P. crinita Thallus glaucous grey with crisp, overlapping, broad, rounded lobes which are frequently much divided along the margin. Black cilia and clumps of coralloid isidia (which are often eroded) are scattered over the surface and along the margins. Undersurface black in the centre, with fine, simple rhizinae, the margins lighter brown with well developed rhizinae. Apothecia are rare. Discs brown with crenulate and often isidiate margins.

Medulla P + o, K + y − r.

Habitat. Locally common in the south-west and west on well-lit trees and rocks. An "old forest" species.

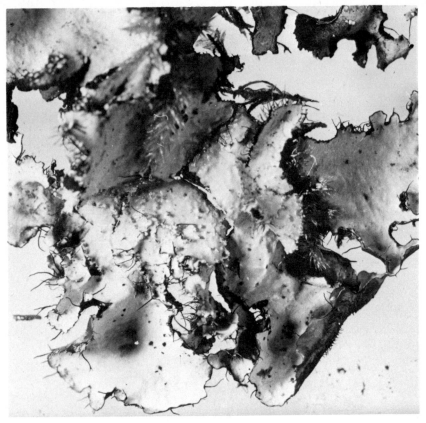

P. crinita x 5

Without isidia or soralia

P. taylorensis Thallus grey, often with a green tinge. Lobes rounded with slightly sinuate notches. Upper surface often white maculate and crumpled. Undersurface very dark brown in the centre, lighter brown at the margin. Dichotomous rhizinae cover the lower surface almost to the extreme edge of the lobes.

Cortex K + y, Medulla C + r. (Note: *P. laevigata* has sorediate lobe tips.)

Habitat. Not uncommon in the south-west on trees and rocks.

P. taylorensis x3.5

P. quercina (P. carporrhizans) Thallus grey, adpressed. Lobes rounded with crenulate tips. Undersurface black with simple rhizinae which grow almost to the tips of the lobes. Usually fertile. Apothecia with red-brown discs and thick margins. The undersurface of the apothecia frequently have black rhizinae (remove to see clearly).

Cortex K + y, Medulla C + r.

Habitat. A very rare and decreasing species, restricted to the sunniest parts of the extreme South of England. Found on well-lit branches, usually in the upper canopy of deciduous woodland.

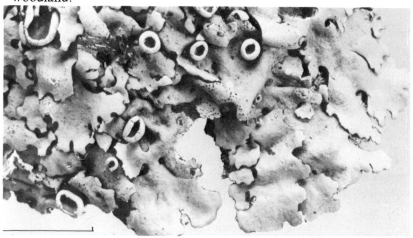

P. quercina x4

THALLUS GREEN-BROWN TO DARK
METALLIC-BROWN
Isidiate, sorediate, or with small warts

P. glabratula Thallus green-brown, shining, adpressed, lobes short, widening at the apices which have shallow notches. Undersurface black in the centre with simple rhizinae, light brown and bare at the apices. Isidia simple or coralloid, becoming crowded in the centre of the thallus. If eroded , leaving white scars.

Medulla C + r, KC + r.

Habitat. Common throughout Britain. Mainly on trees or fences, rarely on rocks.

Subsp. **fuliginosa** is very similar but very dark green-brown to almost black, with dense packed small isidia in the centre, which can almost obscure the lobes.

Habitat. Common on rocks.

P. glabratula x4

P. subaurifera Very similar to *P. glabratula* but often with a more matt surface to the lobes. The isidia are simple and shorter and often break down to form soralia which erode leaving scars which are often yellow-white.

Medulla C + r, KC + r.

Habitat. Very common throughout Britain on trees, fences and sometimes rocks. More frequently found on twigs than *P. glabratula*.

P. subaurifera x5

P. exasperatula Similar to *P. glabratula* but differs in the pale undersurface and negative reactions. It is also more loosely attached to the substrate. Isidia mainly simple but larger and sometimes branched and shaped rather like the bowl of a spoon.

Habitat. Trees, rarely rocks (especially in northern England), usually on slightly nutrient-enriched substrates. *P. laciniatula* is very similar to the previous species but has very narrow lobes (less than 1mm wide) and lacks the isidia.

185

P. exasperatula x16

P. exasperata (P. aspera) Thallus brown to olive–brown, often shiny. Lobes adpressed, short, often widening at the apices, which are rounded and only slightly notched. The lobes often have longitudinal wrinkles and numerous warts with a distinct apical crater (use hand-lens). Undersurface light buff with

very pale simple or squarrose rhizinae. Usually fertile. Discs reddish-brown with thick margins which also bear the warts. Reactions are negative.

Habitat. Common, especially in the west, on twigs and smooth branches of deciduous trees. In other European countries it is normally found growing amongst pine needles, but it has yet to be found on this habitat in Britain.

P. exasperata x5

P. loxodes Thallus green-brown to brown, slightly shiny, lobes long and narrow (2-4mm wide), somewhat convex, parallel sided, not widening or only slightly at the tips, which are rather square cut. The lobe surface with slight transverse wrinkles. Undersurface black with simple or furcate rhizinae, bare

towards the tips of the lobes. Rather spherical isidia form conspicuous laminal clusters that may become confluent and erode to leave prominent white scars.

KC − or red, C −.

Habitat. Frequent in maritime regions in the west on well-lit siliceous rock. The very similar *P. verruculifera (P. isidiotyla)* has more scattered, less confluent and more delicate isidia and more flattened lobes. It is rarer but found in similar habitats.

P. loxodes x 2.5

Without isidia or soralia. Usually fertile

P. omphalodes Thallus brown to grey-brown with a purple almost metallic hue, but often appears lighter as the upper surface is covered in a reticulum of white or pale grey lines. Lobes rather small and expanding greatly at the apices which are notched to give a palmate effect. Undersurface black with simple  or furcate, rather sparse rhizinae which grow almost to the margins of the lobes. Apothecia fairly frequent especially in the north and west. Discs dark brown with a thin, lighter margin. May be separated from *P. saxatilis* and *P. sulcata* by the colour and lack of soralia or isidia.

Medulla K + y − r, P + o. (The much rarer *P. discordans* is mainly westerly and has a less marked reticulum, is less shiny with narrower, more adpressed lobes and is K −)

Habitat. Very common on siliceous rocks, especially in upland areas but extending down to sea level. It was commonly used in dyeing.

P. omphalodes x2.5

P. pulla (P. prolixa) Thallus brown, spreading, slightly shiny, wrinkled, lobes adpressed and not widening at the apices, often covered with a faint reticulum. Undersurface black with sparse, simple rhizinae that often become branched, lobes light brown and bare towards the margins. Apothecia almost always present, dark brown with entire margins when young, becoming thin and much distorted when mature. It resembles a fertile *P. loxodes,* but lack isidia.
Medulla K −, KC −.

Habitat. Common on sunny supralittoral rocks but also more rarely found in upland areas. A separate but rare species, *P. delisei,* is recognised by some authorities. This is lighter brown and medulla is KC + red.

P. pulla x2.5

189

P. acetabulum Thallus leaden-brown, more green when wet, adpressed though inclined to be more erect in the centre of mature specimens. Lobes transversely wrinkled, up to about 8mm wide, rounded and widening at the apices which are deeply notched. Undersurfaces lightish – brown with

rather stout rhizinae that expand at the tip to form a holdfast. Frequently very fertile. Apothecia brown-red with a contorted and inflexed margin.

Medulla K + r, P + orange.

Habitat. Common on somewhat nutrient-rich bark. Mainly in southern and eastern England.

P. acetabulum x5

THALLUS YELLOW-GREEN TO
YELLOWISH-GREY

P. caperata Thallus large, yellow-grey when dry, becoming a very distinctive, almost apple-green when wet. Lobes up to 1cm wide and expanding at the apices. Lobes transversely wrinkled and much contorted when mature, the surface becoming covered in coarse soralia. Undersurface black with often

widely spaced simple rhizinae. The margins of the lobes are light brown below with white rhizinae that turn black as they mature.

Cortex K +y, Medulla P + orange.

Habitat. Very common on deciduous trees in the south but decreasing northwards. It is also found on rocks and mosses, also on conifers in the cleanest air of the extreme south and west.

P. caperata x1.5

P. soredians is very similar to the previous species but is more adpressed. The lobes more incised with granular to farinose soralia which have a distinct K + y to red reaction.

Habitat. Locally frequent on trees in south-east England. It has, however, been found as far west as North Wales, Devon and Ireland.

P. soredians x2.5

P. conspersa Thallus yellow-green to yellow-grey, orbicular. Lobes usually imbricate, narrow, up to 4mm wide and much divided. The surface of the thallus is normally covered in masses of delicate coralloid isidia. Undersurface dark brown to black with usually widely spaced simple rhizinae. Towards the margins the undersurface becomes light brown with brown rhizinae almost to the margins. Commonly fertile. Disc brown, margins thin and contorted.

o   C

Medulla K + y to red, P + o.

Habitat. Common on exposed siliceous rocks and walls in upland regions, but extending down to sea level on maritime rocks, it is also frequently found on dry rocks in streams and lakes.

P. conspersa x4

P. incurva Thallus yellowish-grey, small (up to about 5cm), orbicular, consisting of long narrow (about 2mm wide), radiating convex, contorted lobes which curve under at the tips. These have large rather yellow globose soralia. Undersurface dark brown with simple rhizinae, lighter at the margin.

Medulla KC + r, P −.

Habitat. Locally abundant on siliceous rocks in upland regions.

P. incurva x2

P. mougeotii Resembles the previous species but has narrower (up to about 1mm wide) lobes. The centre of the thallus is dark from the numerous dark brown granules on the surface. Large yellowish-grey, globose soralia are scattered over the surface. Undersurface dark brown to black with simple rhizinae, lighter brown at the margin with rhizinae extending almost to the edge of the lobe.

Medulla K + y, P + o (see *P. incurva*).

Habitat. Not infrequent on siliceous rocks and tombstones in upland regions.

P. mougeottii x3

PARMELIELLA Thallus squamulose, imbricate. The lower surface covered with a thick tomentose, blue-black layer. Apothecia lecideine. Spores colourless, simple, 8 per ascus.

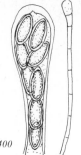

P. plumbea x400

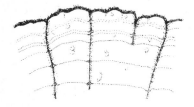

P. plumbea   *P. atlantica*

Usual shape of the thalline ridges

Thallus with dense, grey, coralloid isidia........**P. atlantica**

Thallus lacking isidia.......................................**P. plumbea**

Parmeliella plumbea Thallus light grey when dry, dark grey when wet, forming large dinner plate-like patches when fully developed. The squamules are large with concentric, transverse ridges. There are no isidia. The hypothallus forms a black margin to the thallus. The centre of the thallus is thick and imbricate.

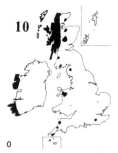

Usually abundantly fertile. Apothecia orange-brown to red-brown, the thin proper margin is soon excluded. It may be separated from the similar *Pannaria rubiginosa* by the larger size, lack of pale margins to the lobes and the lack of a thalline margin.

Habitat. Common on moss covered trees and rocks in the west of Scotland and western Ireland, rare elsewhere.

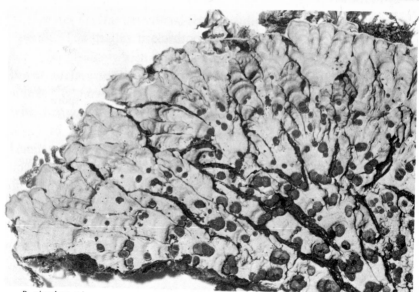

P. plumbea x2

P. atlantica Thallus similar in appearance to the previous species. The ridges are, however, usually fan-shaped and the squamules have rather large grey isidia that become confluent and may cover the surface of the thallus. Apothecia similar to the preceding species but less commonly fertile.

Habitat. As *P. plumbea*, but rarer.

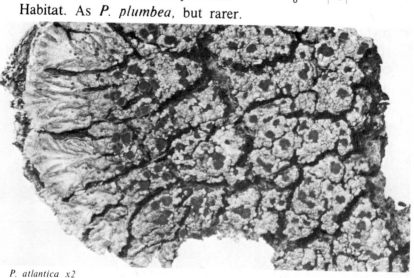

P. atlantica x2

P. albescens May be difficult to separate by sight from the previous species. The soredia however do not have a bitter taste and are always KC −. The soralia are often much larger, more delimited, and more scattered. In var. *corallina* the thallus is thickened in the centre and bears tightly packed, usually eroded isidia.

Habitat. Similar to *P. amara*.

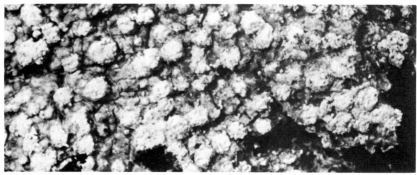

P. albescens x10

P. multipuncta Thallus grey, determinate, thick, smooth or wrinkled. The white soralia differ from the two previous species in being widely dispersed and never forming a more or less sorediate crust and in covering apothecia. K + y, P + o.

Habitat. Common on smooth, acid barked trees (especially young branches), particularly in the south and west.

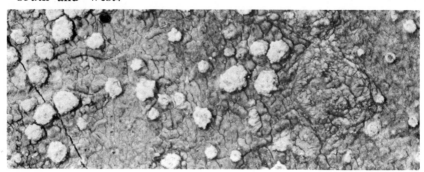

P. multipuncta x1

P. hemisphaerica Thallus blue-grey to yellow-grey. The soralia differ from those of the previous species in being greyish to concolorous with the thallus. Soralia C + r.

Habitat. Locally common on mossy trees, particularly in the west and south and often in slightly shaded sites.

P. hemisphaerica x8

P. flavida Thallus greenish-yellow, warted, usually covered in a dense mass of short, dull yellow isidia which may become eroded. Apothecia extremely rare, small, dark glossy brown with a thick thalline margin.
C + o.

Habitat. Fairly common on rough-barked trees in the south and east.

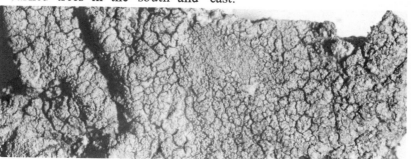

P. flavida x6

207

ISIDIATE, NORMALLY CORTICOLOUS

P. coccodes Thallus grey to yellow-grey, often zoned, thick and areolate, normally with numerous small globose isidia that are concolorous or brown, sometimes on coralloid stalks.

Cortex K + o.

Habitat. An eastern species found mainly on old rough barked trees, but also, rarely on siliceous rock.

P. coccodes x6

LACKING ISIDIA OR SORALIA, FERTILE, CORTICOLOUS

P. pertusa Thallus yellowish-grey, thick and cracked, often limited by a prothallus and concentrically ridged margin. Apothecia are borne in wart-like protruberances (verrucae) several apothecia in each verruca, the discs are apparent as minute darker pits or sometimes opening out slightly.

KC + o, P + o.

Habitat. Very common on trees throughout Britain, but Sometimes also found on siliceous rocks.

C

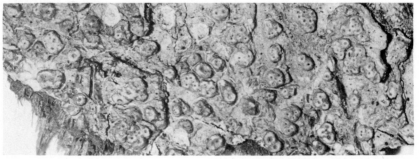

P. pertusa x5

P. hymenea Thallus grey to greenish-grey, thick and wrinkled. Usually fertile. Apothecia often in small groups. The discs are easily seen and much more open than in *P. pertusa,* appearing lecanorine, the margin being thick and crenulate. The disc is concolorous with the thallus to almost flesh pink. KC + o.

Habitat. Common on trees, rarely also on rocks.

7

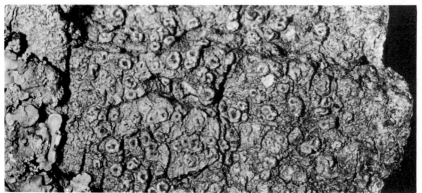

P. hymenea x4

P. leioplaca Thallus creamy grey to green-grey, smooth and cracked or slightly warted. The apothecia are frequently single and arising in warts with an elliptical base.

Habitat. Common on smooth - barked trees in rather shaded situations.

7

P. leioplaca x8

SAXICOLOUS

(See also many of the preceding species which are rather rarely found on rock.)

P. lactea Thallus grey, shining, smooth, areolate or warted, often with a conspicuous white prothallus. Pale cream to pure white, delimited soralia are scattered over the thallus.
Soralia C + r.
Habitat. Frequent on siliceous rocks in upland areas, more rarely overgrowing mosses on rocks.

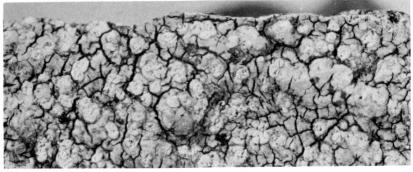

P. lactea x7

P. flavicans Thallus dull sulphur-yellow, thick and often areolate, the delicate isidia erode to rather granular soredia which may become confluent.
Soralia C + r.
Habitat. Locally frequent on well-lit siliceous rocks in the west and north.

P. flavicans x5

P. corallina Thallus white to pale grey, determinate, warted. The surface of the thallus becoming covered with isidia, which can be short and rounded but where well developed coralloid and up to 2mm long (sometimes abraded).
Cortex K + y (persistently yellow), P + r.
Habitat. Very common on exposed siliceous rocks in upland areas.

C

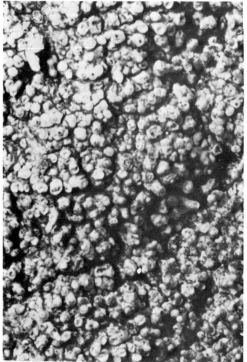

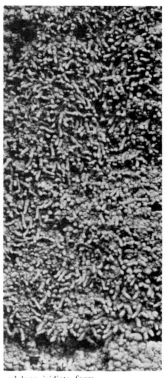

P. corallina x12

x3 long isidiate form

P. pseudocorallina Similar to the previous species but the thallus has a slight yellowish tinge. Generally found with short rather stout, little branched isidia.
Cortex K + y (turning blood–red after some seconds), P + o.
Habitat. Found in similar habitats to *P. corallina*, but perhaps more common than that species in maritime regions.

C

PETRACTIS Thallus crustose. Apothecia lecideine. Spores 8 or more per ascus, colourless, multiseptate. There is only one British species.

P. clausa x600

Petractis clausa Thallus thin, scurfy or endolithic, light grey. Apothecia about 0.5mm across, immersed at first and covered with a thin layer of cortex which splits open to leave small, whiteish teeth around the margin. The disc is concave, pale orange and sunken. The apothecia leave pits in the rock when they fall out. Spores 3 septate.

Habitat. Locally abundant on hard limestone in moderate shade.

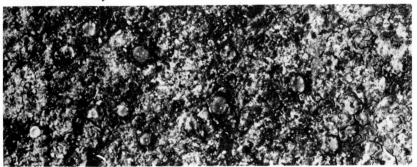

P. clausa x10

PHAEOGRAPHIS Thallus crustose. Phycobiont *Trentepohlia*. Apothecia lirellate, immersed, erumpent, or more rarely sessile. Spores multiseptate, cells thick walled, wider than long, brown (may be colourless when young). The spores help separate this genus from the similar:

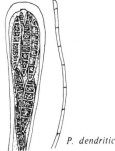

P. dendritica x300

Graphis – spores multiseptate, colourless, thin walled, cells wider than long.

Graphina – spores muriform, colourless, cells wider than long.

Opegrapha – spores multiseptate, colourless, thick walled, cells longer than wide.

1. Thallus white to grey. Lirellae black or pruinose..........2
   Thallus olivaceous–brown. Lirellae brown and pruinose
   ....**P. lyellii**
2. Lirellae wide, innate. Disc with grey-brown pruina
   ....**P. dendritica**
   Lirellae sessile, multifurrowed, black ....**P. ramificans**
   = **Graphis elegans**

Phaeographis dendritica Thallus light grey to almost white and glossy, or slightly granular. Apothecia numerous, elongate and often stellate. Lirellae wide, often with a prominent pseudothalline margin and a relatively wide grey-brown pruinose disc.

K + o unreliable

C

Habitat. Fairly common on smooth barked trees in the west.

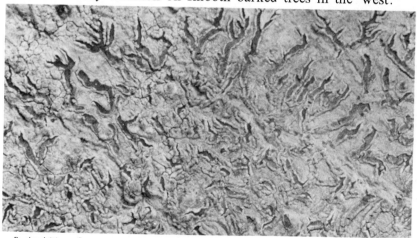

P. dendritica x5

P. ramificans Thallus light grey and glossy, often wrinkled. Apothecia more prominent than in the previous species and often multifurrowed and black.
K + y − o.
Now considered to be *Graphis elegans* in which the spores have turned brown.

213

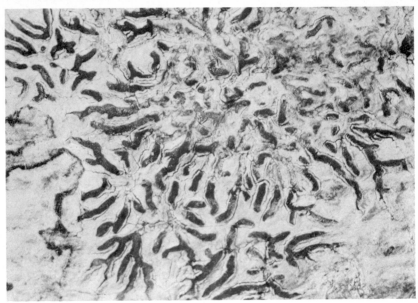

P. ramificans x7

P. lyellii Thallus olivaceous-brown, smooth and glossy. Apothecia open, brown, pruinose, not very prominent and having a thick white powdery margin.

K + y to r.

Habitat. Rare on smooth-barked trees in shade in the south-west of Great Britain and Ireland.

P. lyellii x6

PHLYCTIS Thallus crustose. Apothecia lecanorine, immersed, often difficult to see. Spores, colourless, muriform in British species, normally 2 per ascus.

P. agelaea x250

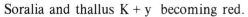

Thallus sorediate, very rarely fertile...................**P. argena**
Thallus not sorediate. Apothecia in powdery depressions
....**P. agelaea**

Phlyctis argena Thallus thin, creamy grey. White to greenish, granular to diffuse soralia cover large areas of the thallus and contrast with the thalline colour, which appears to the naked eye to have been rubbed away in patches. Apothecia very rare.
Soralia and thallus K + y becoming red.
Habitat. Common throughout Britain on well-lit, nutrient-rich trees, shrubs and hedges. Often on the rough nodes of branches.

P. argena x4

P. agelaea Thallus grey, cracked or warted, without soralia but usually fertile. Apothecia being found in powdery warts which only just show the small pink to dark red discs.
K + y becoming red.
Habitat. An often overlooked species of trees in moist situations, especially in the south and west.

215

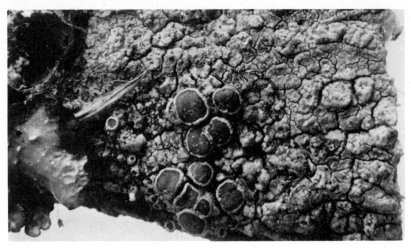

P. agelaea x7

PHYSCIA Thallus foliose with narrow lobes, but sometimes closely adpressed. The upper surface of some species have minute pseudocyphellae. Attached to the substrate by rhizinae. Apothecia lecanorine, discs dark but sometimes pruinose. Spores brown, almost polarilocular, 8 per ascus. The broader lobed, pruinose species are now separated into the genus *Physconia*.

P. pulverulenta x350

1. Thallus without soralia or isidia. Usually fertile............2
   Thallus sorediate or isidiate, less commonly fertile........5
2. Lobes to 1−5mm wide, ascending. Long marginal cilia
   ....**P. leptalea**
   Lobes wider, adpressed. No long marginal cilia.............3
3. Lobes not pruinose. Thallus blue-grey. Med.K + y or −..4
   Lobe tips pruinose. Thallus grey-brown to greenish.
   Medulla K −..**P. pulverulenta**
4. Thallus with pale pseudocyphellae. Medulla K + y
   ....**P. aipolia**
   Thallus without pseudocyphellae. Medulla K −. (Rare)
   ....**P. stellaris**
5. Medulla K + y. Isidiate, if sorediate, soralia grey with blue

flecks..6

Medulla K −. Not isidiate but with soralia....................9

6. Soralia convex, grey usually with blue flecks. Thallus pseudocyphellate, forming blue-grey rosettes.......**P. caesia**
Thallus isidiate 7

7. Thallus grey, erect incised lobes. Isidia globular **P. tribacia**
Thallus adpressed. Isidia granular to coralloid................8

8. Lobes broad, white, brown or green, pruinose. Isidia coarse, granular, initially marginal......................**P. grisea**
Lobes very narrow, pale grey, not pruinose. Isidia fine and coralloid, initially central............................... **P. clementei**

9. Lobes to 1mm wide ascending. Long concolorous marginal cilia (often with dark tips)..10
Lobes wider and/or lacking concolorous cilia..............11

10. Lobe lips inflated and splitting to expose soredia
....**P. adscendens**
Lobe tips not inflated. Soredia on lower surface of lobe tip
....**P. tenella**

11. Adpressed, lobes little divided. Thallus colour various, greenish when wet...12
Lobes erect and much divided. Pale grey.......**P. tribacia**

12. Dry lobes brownish-grey to black, narrow, not pruinose, often with dark cilia. Soralia globose, with dark flecks
....**P. orbicularis**
Dry lobes grey to brown,broader, pruinose, no cilia. Soralia granulose, concolorous ....**P. grisea**

FERTILE NOT SOREDIATE

Physcia aipolia Thallus blue-grey, lobes with distinct pale pseudocyphellae (use hand lens). The lobes growing together and their outlines becoming indistinct in the centre of the thallus. Undersurface with black rhizinae. Apothecia usually abundant and becoming large (up to 3 mm), prominent with a thick thalline

margin. Discs dark brown to black becoming convex, sometimes pruinose.

Medulla K + y.

Habitat. Common throughout Britain on well-lit, nutrient-rich trees, shrubs and hedges. Often on the rough nodes of branches

P. stellaris This is a very similar rare northern species, but the medulla lacks atranorin (K −), and the lobes do not have maculate pseudocyphellae.

P. aipolia x8

P. pulverulenta [Physconia pulverulenta] Thallus grey to brown when dry, bright green when wet, orbicular, up to 10cm across. Lobes rather palmate, overlapping, white pruinose especially at the tips. Often with many small lobules in the centre of the thallus. No pseudocyphellae. Undersurface light  brown to black with rhizinae. Apothecia very common and up to about 3mm across. Discs brown to black and covered in a coarse pruina that looks like icing sugar. The thick thalline margin may become lobate. This species is easily separated from *P. aipolia* by the pruina, the normally brown disc, lack of pseudocyphellae and the K − reaction.

Habitat. Common, especially in the west, on nutrient-rich bark and exceptionally on rock, often over mosses.

P. pulverulenta x3

P. leptalea [P. semipinnata] Thallus light grey, lobes long and narrow (about 1mm wide), mostly ascending, very pseudocyphellate, and bearing long marginal cilia, especially towards the lobe tips. Undersurface white with a few scattered rhizinae. Often fertile, the apothecia with tumid margins, discs

frequently very pruinose. Young specimens of *P. adscendens* and *P. tenella* resemble this species but may be separated as they mature by the presence of soralia on these species. K + y.

Habitat. A rather local species, found on trees and shrubs mainly in the south and west, exceptionally on rock.

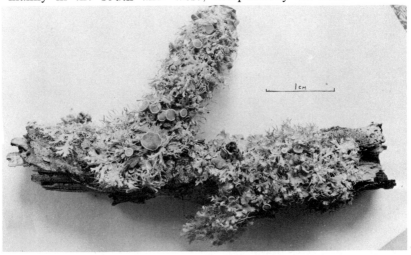

P. leptalea x2

SOREDIATE, MOSTLY INFERTILE

P. adscendens Thallus light grey, seldom more than 2cm across. The lobes less than 1mm wide with no pseudocyphellae, lobe tips erect and with long marginal cilia. Undersurface white with scattered rhizinae. The lobe ends become hood-shaped and inflated, bursting along the lower surface to

expose a mass of cream to yellowish soredia contained inside the inflated tip. When fertile the discs are black and pruinose with tumid margins.

K + y.

Habitat. Very common throughout Britain on nutrient-rich trees, calcareous rocks, tombstones, asbestos-cement, etc.

Lobe tip of
P. tenella

Lobe tip of
P. adscendens

P. adscendens x15

P. tenella Very similar to the preceding species from which it differs in the lobe ends, which are not hood-shaped but split and turn back to reveal the rather coarse, cream coloured soredia.
K + y.
Habitat. Similar to *P. adscendens* but generally less frequent.

C

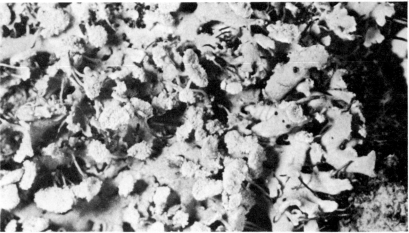

P. tenella x10

P. caesia Thallus characteristic bluish-grey, matt, orbicular, very strongly adpressed, pseudocyphellate. Lobes strongly convex, often overlapping and becoming less clear in the centre of the thallus. It may be recognised by the globular masses of granular to farinose soralia which are light grey often with

dirty blue flecks in them. The soralia occur over the lobes, especially in the centre of the thallus, but never at the lobe ends. Undersurface white to tan with scattered buff to black rhizinae. Medulla K + y.
Habitat. Very common throughout Britain on nutrient-enriched rocks, asbestos-cement, tombstones, and more rarely on trees or wood. Two rare but similar species found in unpolluted areas are: *P. teretiuscula [P. dubia]* which has long narrow (less than 1mm wide) lobes that are clearly separated from each

other and becoming palmate at the tips. The soralia are more inclined to be apical than in *P. caesia*. Found in the west of Britain. *P. wainioi,* is less adpressed in the centre with marginal or apical soralia which are volcano-shaped, not globular when mature.

The medulla of both species is K + y and they are found in less nutrient-enriched sites than *P. caesia.*

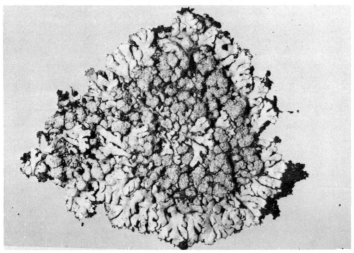

P. caesia x4

P. orbicularis [Phaeophyscia orbicularis]

Thallus very variable in colour from pale brownish-grey to brown or almost black. When wet the paler specimens become a rather vivid green. The thallus is orbicular or dispersed and irregular, adpressed. Lobes long and becoming palmately divided at the tip. Lower surface normally black, but may be pale buff, with dark rhizinae that become ciliate at the margins. Soralia white or cream to greenish with blue to black areas, less globose and smaller than in *P. caesia* from which it may be separated by the thallus colour and the reaction.

Medulla K −.

Habitat. Very common in similar habitats to *P. caesia,* but more easily overlooked as it often consists of small scattered lobes.

P. orbicularis x6

P. grisea [Physconia grisea] Thallus white, grey or brown, green when wet, usually coarsely pruinose. Lobes up to 3mm wide, short, overlapping and palmate at the tips, parts of the lobe tips often turn upwards. Undersurface almost white with pale rhizinae. Soralia are coarsely granular and appear isidiate in many specimens

Medulla K −.

Habitat. Common throughout Britain on nutrient-rich trees, tombstones and rocks, often overgrowing mosses.

P. grisea x8

P. tribacia Thallus light grey, forming a mat of erect, contorted and incised lobes up to 1mm wide (rarely 2-3mm). Laminal and apical globular isidia are present which may break down to soredia. Undersurfaces white to pale tan with a few light coloured rhizinae. Medulla K −.

Habitat. Not infrequent on rocks and trees in nutrient-enriched sites, particularly in south-east England.

P. tribacia x8

P. clementei Thallus light grey, closely adpressed, orbicular. Lobe tips rather wrinkled. Undersurface white with a few light rhizinae. The centre of the thallus is densely covered in isidia (which may break down to form soredia). When fertile, the apothecia have thick slightly crenulate margins and pruinose discs. Medulla K + y.

Habitat. Now very rare but locally abundant in the south-west on nutrient-rich trees (sometimes wood), walls and rocks.

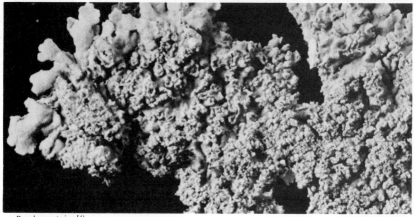

P. clementei x10

PHYSCIOPSIS This genus differs from *Physcia* in the long thin curved conidia, those in *Physcia* being short and not bent. It also differs in colour and size. There is only one British species.

Physciopsis adglutinata Thallus greenish-brown, small (only about 1.5cm across), however, individual thalli coalesce and then cover large areas. Lobes long and less than 1.5mm wide, palmate at the tips. The upper surface splits and greenish soredia fill the crater-shaped soralia.

Medulla K −.

Habitat. Not uncommon in the south and west on rather shaded trees (especially elder), very rarely also on nutrient-enriched siliceous rocks.

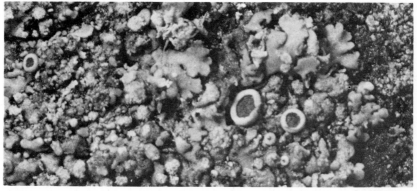

P. adglutinata x6

PILOPHORUS Primary thallus crustose. Phycobiont *Trebouxia* but cephalodia containing blue-green algae also present. The lecideine apothecia are found on short coralloid podetia. Spores simple, colourless, 8 per ascus. It may be separated when fertile from similar genera in Britain as follows:

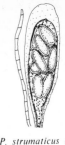

P. strumaticus x300

    Cladonia – hollow podetia.
    Baeomyces – no algae in podetia, spores multiseptate.
    Stereocaulon – podetia more branched, spores multiseptate.

There is only one British species.

Pilophorus strumaticus (P. distans) Primary thallus grey, coarsely granular, almost squamulose, but may become areolate. Usually with dark brown cepholodia scattered over the surface. The rare black apothecia are borne on short podetia up to about 5mm high.

K + y.
Habitat. A local species of damp shaded rocks in upland areas of the extreme west.

P. strumaticus x10

PLACOPSIS Thallus crustose to placodioid. Cephalodia containing blue-green algae are usually present. It was previously placed in the genus *Lecanora*. The spores are simple, colourless, 8 per ascus. There is only one British species.

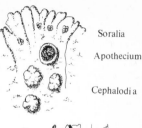

Soralia

Apothecium

Cephalodia

Placopsis gelida Thallus bluish-grey to pale brown-grey, areolate centrally but becoming placodioid towards the margin. Convex, conspicuous, pink to brown cephalodia are scattered over the surface and small delimited soralia which become abraded are also found. Apothecia fairly common with a rather thick thalline margin and a dark red-brown disc. Cortex K + y, C + r, Medulla KC + r.

Habitat. A rather local species of upland regions on shaded or sometimes exposed, damp siliceous rocks.

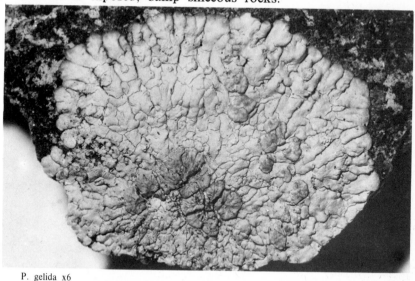

P. gelida x6

PLACYNTHIUM Thallus crustose or slightly placodioid, homoiomerous. Phycobiont blue-green. Apothecia lecideine. Spores colourless, septate, 8 per ascus.

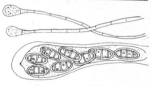

P. nigrum x400

Placynthium nigrum Thallus dark brown or more usually black to blue-black, consisting of very small granules often less than 0.1mm across and giving a coralloid appearance (use hand lens), sometimes smooth and cracked especially in polluted areas. The thallus is delimited by a wide dark blue, felted

4

0

prothallus. Apothecia, when present, less than 1mm diameter, black with a glossy disc. Spores up to 3 septate.

Habitat. Very common, mainly on rather hard calcareous substrates throughout Britain. Often found on tombstones, cement, but not asbestos.

P. nigrum x12

PLATISMATIA Foliose, undersurface may have a few scattered rhizinae, but they are usually absent. Apothecia lecanorine. Spores simple, colourless, 8 per ascus. It differs from *Cetraria* in the cells of the upper cortex and in the fact that atranorin predominates whilst in *Cetraria* it does not and fatty acids

P. glauca x600

commonly occur. It differs from *Parmelia* in the marginal apothecia and pycnidia, (in *Parmelia* they are laminal).

Platismatia glauca Thallus grey to brownish-green (little changed when wet). Lobes up to 4cm long, erect with crisp margins, often rather tufted. Upper surface somewhat shining and often with thin white cracks. The incised lobe margins are frequently fringed with isidia or coarse soralia. Undersurface white becoming brown towards the centre. (The superficially similar but smaller *Cetraria chlorophylla* has a brown undersurface which frequently becomes paler towards the centre.) Usually without rhizinae but sometimes with a few thick, divided rhizinae towards the centre. Apothecia rare, disc red-brown with a thin margin.
K + y.

Habitat. Very common mainly in upland areas on acidic-barked trees and siliceous rocks. Particularly in moderately polluted areas.

P. glauca x2

POLYBLASTIA Thallus crustose or immersed, saxicolous or terricolous. Perithecia single or multiple, superficial or immersed in the substrate. Spores colourless or brown, muriform, mainly 8 per ascus. None of the species are common in Britain.
They may be separated from some superficially similar genera as follows:

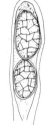

P. tristicula x150

Verrucaria – simple, colourless spores.

Thelidium – 1-3 septate (sometimes appearing slightly muriform), colourless to brown spores.

Staurothele – muriform, colourless to brown spores, but with algal cells in the hymenium.

Porina – multiseptate, colourless spores.

1. Thallus dark green-brown. Peritheca over 0.5mm **P. cruenta**
   Thallus white to apple-brown or greenish. Perithecia to 0.5mm 2
2. Thallus white or pale grey. Perithecia in pits. Spores 8 per ascus ....**P. albida**
   Thallus pale brown to greenish. Perithecia prominent. Spores 2 per ascus ....**P. tristicula**

Polyblastia albida Thallus white or light grey, rather scurfy or evanescent, sometimes limited by a black prothallus. Perithecia immersed in pits, very small (up to about 0.25mm). Spores colourless, 8 per ascus.
Habitat. Infrequent on shaded hard limestone or mortar in both lowland and upland Britain.

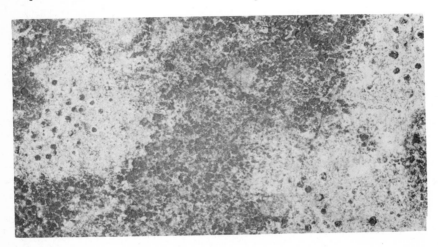

P. albida x8

P. cruenta (P. henscheliana) Thallus dark brownish-green, cracked, thin or almost evanescent. Perithecia appearing as warts with a small dark ostiole. Spores mainly brown, 8 per ascus. Habitat. Not infrequent on siliceous rocks in streams in upland Britain, especially in the west. It is doubtfully distinct from *P. inumbrata*, a rare species of exposed calcareous rocks in the Scottish Highlands.

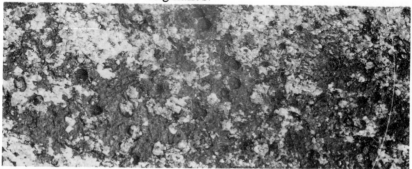

P. cruenta x8

P. tristicula [Agonimia tristicula] Thallus pale brown to grey-brown, greenish when wet, granular or rather squamulose. The granules have cortical cells with characteristic minute papillate projections. Perithecia small (about 0.25mm), but prominent. Spores colourless, 2 per ascus.

Habitat. Not infrequent in upland regions but especially in the south and west. Found mainly on mosses and earth on rocks, on church walls and on trees.

squamules x35

cortical cells x2000

P. tristicula x12

231

PORINA Thallus crustose or immersed. Phycobiont *Trentepohlia*. Perithecia usually compound. Spores colourless, from 1, but usually 3 or more septate. 8 per ascus.

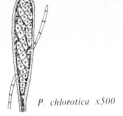

P. chlorotica x500

Thallus brown to greenish black. Perithecia black c.0.5mm wide..**P. chlorotica**
Thallus grey to brown. Perithecia pale pink to dark brown c. 0.25mm wide...**P. leptalea**

Porina chlorotica Thallus brown to greenish — black, thin, smooth or irregularly cracked, often with a black prothallus. Perithecia up to about 0.5mm, prominent, rather glossy black. Spores 3 septate.

Habitat. var. *chlorotica* is common on damp shaded rocks in upland regions, rare in the lowlands.

var. *persicina [P. linearis]* is not infrequent. Thallus creamy-grey with a pinkish tinge and is found on hard limestone. P. *carpinea* has a thin, dark brown, often poorly delimited thallus with very small (about 0.2mm), glossy black perithecia. It is found on smooth-barked trees, mainly in the west.

P. chlorotica x10

P. leptalea Thallus grey to brown or evanescent. Perithecia small (up to about 0.25mm). pale pinkish-brown to chestnut or darker, often irregular in outline. Spores 3 septate.

Habitat. An often overlooked species of deciduous trees, especially smooth barked species in damp areas, mainly in the west.

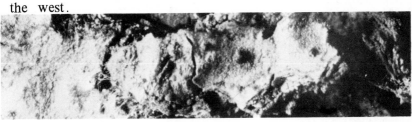

P. leptalea x15

PROTOBLASTENIA Thallus crustose, saxicolous. Apothecia lecideine often orange or red and K + p. Spores simple, colourless, 8 per ascus. *Caloplaca* species differ in their one septate spores.

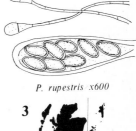

P. rupestris x600

Protoblastenia rupestris Thallus white to grey, scurfy, areolate or almost absent. Apothecia orange, sessile, about 1mm wide becoming very convex and distorted, a faint paler margin is sometimes visible.

Apothecia K + p.

Habitat. Common on mortar and other calcareous substrates.

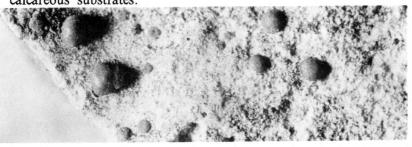

P. rupestris x10

PSEUDEVERNIA Thallus foliose, strap shaped, often ascending so as to appear fruticose. Apothecia lecanorine, spores simple, colourless, 8 per ascus. This genus was formerly included in *Parmelia* but is separated from it by the strap-like lobes and the absence of rhizinae.

P. furfuracea x1200

Pseudevernia furfuracea Thallus grey, ascendent to pendant. The upper surface with isidia or small lobules. The margins of the lobes curl under to almost cover the usually black (white under the youngest lobes) undersurface. Apothecia in the nineteenth century were not infrequent in British specimens, but are almost unknown in this century.

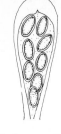

There are two chemical races:
Cortex K + y, medulla C −, KC + rose-red [var. *furfuracea*].
Cortex K + y, medulla C + rose, Kc + red [var. *ceratea*].
Habitat. Common on siliceous rocks, acidic-barked trees and fences in upland and northern areas. Very rare in lowland Britain (where it is usually on fences). At one time it was used to stop haemorrhage.

P. furfuracea x2

PSEUDOCYPHELLARIA. Thallus foliose, lower surface tomentose with pseudocyphellae, upper surface often sorediate, very rarely fertile in Britain. Apothecia lecanorine. Spores brown, up to 3 septate, 8 per ascus. This genus was once included in *Sticta* to which it is closely related, however, as the name suggests, the pores on the lower surface differ in structure; there are also differences in chemistry.

Yellow pseudocyphellae, yellowish soralia.........**P. crocata**
Small white pseudocyphellae, bluish-grey soralia
....**P. thouarsii**

Pseudocyphellaria thouarsii [P. intricata] Thallus brown, grey when dry, lobes large and incised, margins with bluish-grey soralia which sometimes spread over the surface of the lobe. Undersurface tomentose, brown with small white pseudocyphellae, which may be difficult to detect.

Habitat. Very rare on moss-covered trees, rocks and heather stems in western Scotland and south-west Ireland.

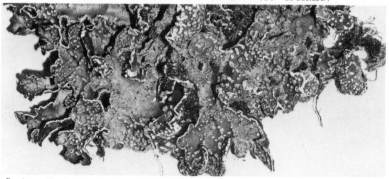

P. thouarsii x4

P. crocata Thallus similar to the previous species but usually smaller, greener when wet. May be separated by the conspicuous yellow pseudocyphellae and yellowish medulla and soralia.
Habitat. As the previous species but slightly less rare.

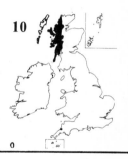

235

PSOROMA Thallus squamulose or lobate. Apothecia lecanorine. Spores colourless, simple, 8 per ascus. This genus is related to *Pannaria*.

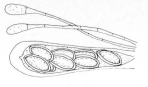

P. hypnorum x350

Psoroma hypnorum Thallus green to orange-brown, consisting of small lobes fixed to the substrate in the centre by fine dark rhizinae. Apothecia develop one to a lobe, red-brown, up to 4mm across, concave at first but becoming plane. The apothecia when mature occupy the whole of the lobe leaving only a thin margin of the squamule.

Habitat. Not common. Found on damp shaded trees, rocks and soil.

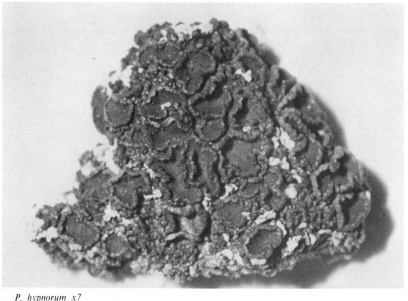

P. hypnorum x7

PYCNOTHELIA Primary thallus crustose. Podedia short, digitate and hollow. Apothecia lecideine. Spores colourless, simple, 8 per ascus. There is only one species and this was formerly included in *Cladonia*.

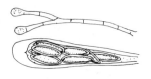

P. papillaria x1200

Pycnothelia papillaria Primary thallus grey, crustose. Persistent podetia arise from the primary thallus, these are cylindrical, hollow, simple or slightly branched, pale purplish-brown and often densely packed, up to 1.5cm high. Often tipped with brown apothecia or more commonly dark pycnidia.
K + distinct yellow.
Habitat. Common on wet peat moors in the north and west, rarer elsewhere.

P. papillaria x3

PYRENULA Thallus crustose, found on smooth-barked trees. Perithecia volcano-shaped to globular. Spores brown, to 5 septate with distinctive locules, 8 per ascus. Mainly a tropical genus with only five species currently accepted as British.

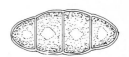

P. nitida x1500

Perithecia about 1mm diam. ....**P. nitida**
Perithecia up to 0.5mm diam. ....**P. nitidella**

Pyrenula nitida Thallus waxy, creamy-yellow to greenish-brown, small, with white flecks scattered over the thallus (use hand lens). It often forms mosaics, individual thalli being separated by a pronounced black prothallus. Perithecia up to 1mm across, globose, becoming prominent when mature with a clearly

visible ostiole (use hand lens). Spores brown, 3 septate with very distinctive shaped locules.

Habitat. Common on shaded, smooth-barked trees, especially in the south and west, decreasing northwards.

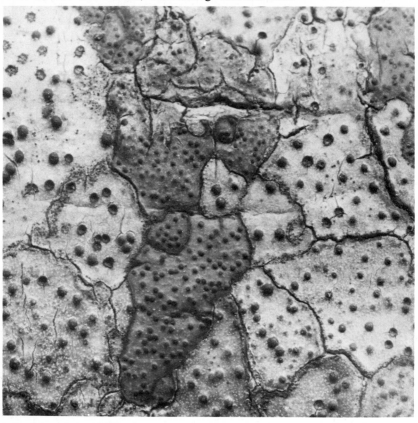

P. nitida and *P. nitidella* x4

P. nitidella Resembles the previous species with which it frequently grows, but differs primarily in the perithecia being only about 0.5mm diameter. It also frequently has a slightly darker thallus. Habitat. Common in similar habitats to *P. nitida*. Another British species currently recognised is *P. laevigata* which differs from *P. nitidella* in the pale thallus with a less pronounced prothallus. It is rare and westerly, mainly in north - west Scotland.

RACODIUM Thallus consisting of a mat of filamentous strands, each consisting of an algal filament surrounded by dark fungal hyphae. These hyphae are arranged parallel to the algal filament, and in this it differs from *Cystocoleus* where the hyphae are irregularly arranged to give an uneven, wavy appearance under the microscope. There is only one British species.

R. rupestre x150

Racodium rupestre Thallus dark brown to black, felted. The fungal hyphae surrounding the algal cells are straight and more or less parallel. Frequently found growing with *Cystocoleus niger* and *Lepraria incana.*

Habitat. Common especially in the north and west, on more or less vertical shaded siliceous rocks.

RAMALINA Thallus fruticose, greenish-grey to yellowish-grey, more or less flattened, upper and lower surfaces similar, tufted pendent. Apothecia lecanorine, fawn coloured. Spores colourless, one septate, 8 per ascus. All species contain some usnic acid (sometimes very difficult to detect). They have been used for a number of purposes including being ground up to make a hair powder.

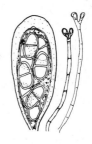

R. calicaris x600

1   Sorediate, normally infertile..2

    Lacking soredia, mainly found fertile............................4

2. Soralia marginal, not in inflated lobe tips.....................3

    Lobe tips inflated and splits to reveal contained soredia

    ......:..**R. baltica**

3. Medulla and soralia K −. (Very common)......**R. farinacea**

239

Medulla and soralia K + yellow to red ......**R. subfarinacea**
4. Corticolous, not very brittle..5
    Saxicolous, brittle, usually maritime 7
5. Lobes strap-shaped, erect or pendent. Apothecia mainly at
    or near lobe tips...6
    Lobes short and bushy, usually covered with apothecia at
    tips ....**R. fastigiata**
6. Lobes narrow with channels (caniculate).........**R. calicaris**
    Lobes widen from the base, wrinkled but not caniculate
    ....**R. fraxinea**
7. Thallus erect or slightly pendent, pitted, not blackened at
    base. Pycnidia with black tips ....**R. siliquosa**
    Thallus pendent, more or less smooth, usually blackened at
    base. Pycnidia with white tips........................**R. cuspidata**

SOREDIATE

Ramalina farinacea. Thallus variable, consisting of pale grey-green to yellow-green, flattened branches, often weakly caniculate, to about 5cm long. Farinose soredia are found along the margins of the branches in disc-like soralia.
Medulla and soralia K −.
Habitat. The commonest of the British species of *Ramalina* and the most tolerant to air pollution. Usually found on nutrient-rich bark, sometimes on rocks.

5

0

R. farinacea x2

R. subfarinacea Similar to the preceding species but usually smaller with much divided branches giving it a bushy appearance, it has a more yellow colour and more excavate soralia. Mainly found on rocks in maritime regions, it is separated by the K+ yellow to red reaction of the medulla and soralia.

R. baltica (R. obtusata) Thallus grey-green, only slightly branched with wrinkled lobes up to 1cm wide. The lobe tips become inflated and split open to reveal the farinose soredia inside.
Habitat. Nutrient-rich trees, rocks and stone walls, especially in pastures and farms.

R. baltica x3

LACKING SOREDIA

R. siliquosa Thallus erect or pendent, very variable. Glossy or warted, pale yellow-grey to greenish-grey, branches scimitar-shaped, brittle and little divided above the base. Often fertile with pale fawn discs. Pycnidia tips black. Known locally as "sea ivory", it is eaten by sheep in Shetland.

Habitat. Very common on hard siliceous rocks in maritime districts above high-water mark, inland in exposed sites in regions subject to maritime influence.

R. siliquosa x2

R. cuspidata (R. curnowii) Similar to the preceding species but distinctly pendent and more or less terete, more yellowish in colour and blackened at the base. Pycnidia tips white. Not found inland.

R. calicaris Thallus grey-green, up to about 8cm long with narrow divided branches having turned up edges to give a deep single channel (caniculate). Almost always fertile. Apothecia fawn-coloured, on or near the tips of the branches. Spores straight.

Habitat. Common on nutrient-rich bark.

R. calicaris x1

R. fraxinea Poorly developed specimens resemble the preceding species, but most branches usually widen out from the base and are not caniculate. Well developed specimens have wide, coarsely wrinkled branches that have marginal and apical apothecia with pale fawn-coloured discs.

Habitat. Common on nutrient-rich bark, becoming rarer.

R. fraxinea x1

R. fastigiata Thallus more or less erect and tufted, up to 4cm high .but usually shorter. Lobes branched, rounded, swollen, bearing apical apothecia that may be so numerous as to almost conceal the thallus.

Habitat. Common on nutrient-rich bark.

R. fastigiata x2

RHIZOCARPON Thallus crustose, saxicolous, usually with a distinct prothallus. Apothecia dark brown to black, lecideine, generally immersed in the thallus. Spores brown when mature, usually muriform but one septate to multiseptate in a few species. 8 or less per ascus.

R. obscuratum x450

1. Thallus chalky-white, rather basic rocks, apothecia often in concentric rings...**R. petraeum**
   Thallus not pure white, siliceous substrates....................2

2. Thallus yellow-green........................**R. geographicum** agg.
   Thallus grey, brown or rust coloured............................3

3. Thallus rust - coloured, apothecial margins convoluted
   ....**R. oederi**
   Thallus grey or brown...4

4. Thallus chocolate − brown, cortex C + red (maritime)
   ....**R. constrictum**
   Thallus grey or brown-grey, cortex C − 5

5. Mature spores muriform, margins of apothecia distinct
   ....**R. obscuratum**
   Mature spores one septate, margins of apothecia narrow or
   excluded ....**R. hochstetteri**

Rhizocarpon geographicum agg. Thallus bright yellow-green to almost yellow, glossy with a pronounced black prothallus showing between the areolae and limiting the thallus. It is often mosaic forming. A rather variable complex. Apothecia black, innate, usually irregular in shape. Spores brown and muriform when mature.

Habitat. A very common species of hard siliceous rocks, especially in upland regions. Its distinctive colouration enables it to be often recognised at a distance.

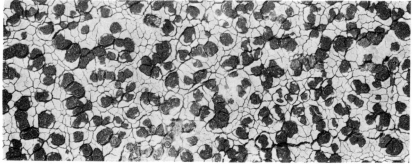

R. geographicum x8

R. obscuratum Thallus grey to mouse-brown, often rather scabrid with a thin black prothallus. Apothecia innate becoming sessile, black with a pronounced proper margin, about 1mm across. May be confused with *Fuscidea cyathoides* from which it differs in its septate to muriform brown spores, the

6

P − medulla, less regularly areolate thallus, and apothecia which are less distinctly marginate and often convex.
Habitat. Very common on smooth siliceous rocks and pebbles.

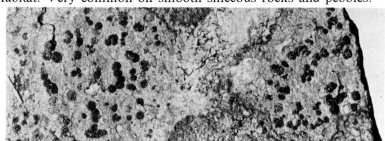

R. obscuratum x3.5

R. constrictum Thallus chocolate-brown to brownish-grey, cracked, sometimes with a fimbriate brown-black prothallus. Apothecia innate, plane, black with a thin proper margin. Spores mainly one septate, but some often have a few longitudinal septa.
Cortex C + red. This reaction separates it

C

from the superficially similar *R. hochstetteri* and *R. obscuratum*.
Habitat. Very common on siliceous rocks in maritime areas in the south-west.

245

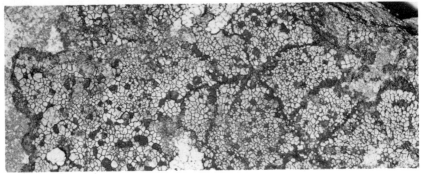

R. constrictum x4

R. hochstetteri Thallus brown-grey to very dark brown, cracked, smooth, on a brown-black prothallus. Apothecia black, innate with a thin proper margin that becomes excluded. Spores brown, one septate.
Cortex C −.
Habitat. Occasional in upland regions of Britain on slightly basic siliceous rocks; rather rare in maritime regions.

R. hochstetteri x6

R. oederi Thallus rust-coloured, regularly areolate, with a black prothallus. Apothecia less than 0.75mm diam, concave, the proper margin becoming convoluted, serpentine or almost gyrose when old. Spores pale brown, 3 septate. Habitat. Common on metal-rich siliceous rocks in upland areas. *Lecidea*

atrata is found on similar rocks and also has a rust-red thallus. It may be separated by its simple spores.

R. oederi x6

R. petraeum Thallus chalky-white, matt, cracked, areolate in the centre. Apothecia up to about 2mm diam, innate, irregular in shape, often arranged in concentric rings. Disc black and rough with a slightly paler or pruinose margin. Spores brown, muriform.
Habitat. Widely distributed on slightly basic siliceous rocks.

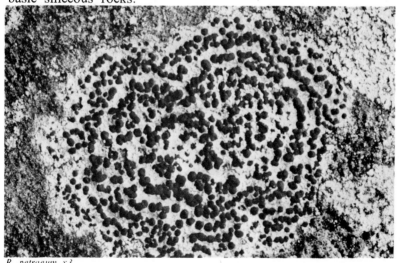

R. petraeum x3

RINODINA Thallus crustose, often limited by a dark prothallus. Apothecia lecanorine with black discs. Spores brown, mainly polarilocular, to 3 septate, 8 per ascus. A number of rare species are found on rock in Britain.

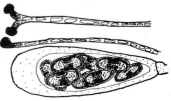

R. subexigua x900

247

1. Saxicolous (this is the only common species in non-maritime areas)..................................**R. subexigua**
   Corticolous...2

2. Apothecia less than 0.75mm diam, on rough bark...**R. exigua**
   Apothecia 1mm diam or larger..............................3

3. Found on rough bark, K + y ....**R. roboris**
   Found on twigs and smooth bark, K −...........**R. sophodes**

Corticolous

Rinodina roboris Thallus grey to grey-green, granular, thick. The black prothallus can often be seen between the outer warty granules as well as around the circumference. Usually abundantly fertile. Apothecia sessile with a thick pale thalline margin. Discs black and rough. Spores one septate. K + y.

Habitat. Common on deciduous mainly rough-barked trees in the south, becoming less common northwards. It may be separated from similar rarer species by the size of the apothecia and the reactions with K (see key above).

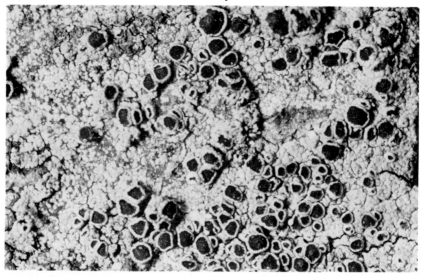

R. roboris x8

Saxicolous

R. subexigua Thallus grey to brown-grey, granular areolate or frequently almost absent. Apothecia about 0.5mm diam, sessile with brown-black discs and a thick, pale, thalline margin in young fruits which may become excluded with age. Spores one septate. K −.

Habitat. Common on calcareous or other basic or nutrient-enriched rocks, walls, bricks or asbestos-cement.

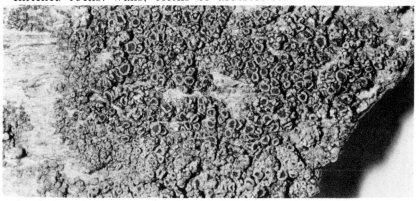

R. subexigua x6

ROCCELLA Thallus pale fawn to bluish-grey, cylindrical or strap − shaped, attached by a basal sheath. Apothecia extremely rare in British species. Discs black. Spores colourless, elongate-ellipsoid, multiseptate. This is a large genus widely distributed in warmer latitudes, but only two species are found

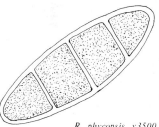

R. phycopsis x3500

as far north as Britain. Roccella species (but not the British ones) are used to produce litmus and the purple dye orchil. The best known species for this purpose being *R. tinctoria* and *R. montagnei*. British species may be separated from *Ramalina siliquosa*, with which they often grow, by the thallus colour and the C + red reaction. The British species are rare and should not be collected.

Thallus pendent, flattened. Medulla C −, soralia C + red
....**R. fuciformis**
Thallus erect or slightly pendent, terete. Medulla C + red,
soralia C − ....**R. phycopsis**

Roccella fuciformis Thallus pendulous, up to 15cm long, bluish – grey and irregularly branched, flattened, strap-shaped, less than 1cm wide, with convex glaucous or brownish – white soralia, medulla white within the holdfast. Apothecia very rare in Britain. Spores 3 septate.

Cortex and medulla C −, soralia C + bright red.
Habitat. A rather rare species of dry sheltered crevices in supralittoral rocks in the extreme south – west. Frequently found with *R. phycopsis.*

R. fuciformis x 2

R. phycopsis Thallus tufted, not or scarcely pendent, usually not exceeding 5cm long, branches more or less terete, with pale glaucous soralia, medulla often yellowish within the holdfast.
Cortex C + rose-red, soralia C −.
Habitat. As *R. fuciformis,* but somewhat more frequent, it is also found on tombstones and walls.

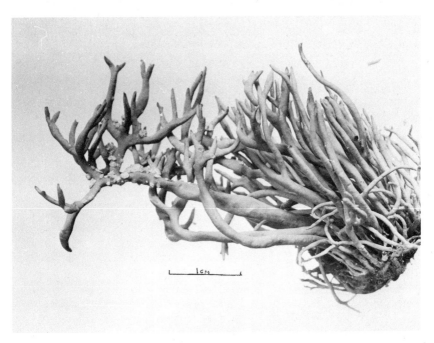

R. phycopsis x2

SARCOGYNE Thallus crustose, evanescent or endolithic. Apothecia lecideine. Spores colourless, simple, small and very many (100 +) per ascus. Thallus reactions negative.

S. simplex x450

Calcareous substrates, apothecia often pruinose ....S. regularis
Siliceous substrates, apothecia not pruinose, margins wide and very crenulate, almost gyrose ....S. simplex

Sarcogyne regularis Thallus pale grey, frequently evanescent. Apothecia up to 0.75mm diam. Disc black or when wet chestnut to dark red, often pruinose, margins becoming crenulate.
Habitat. Common on calcareous substrates especially in upland regions.

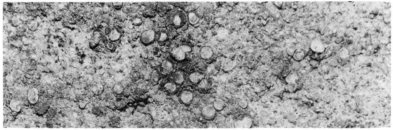

S. regularis x5

S. simplex Thallus pale grey, frequently evanescent. Apothecia to 0.5mm diam. Disc black, or when wet, dark red, not pruinose, margins black, wide, very crenulate and often reaching over the disc giving it an almost gyrose appearance.

Habitat. Rather common on acid rocks in upland regions.

6

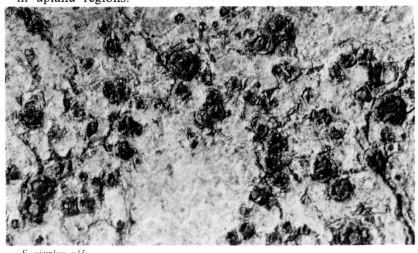

S. simplex x15

SCLEROPHYTON Thallus crustose, areolate with a dark prothallus. Apothecia lecideine, immersed, very small and usually arranged in lines. Spores brown, 5-7 septate, 8 per ascus. This is mainly a tropical genus and is represented in Britain by only one species.

S. circumscriptum x350

Sclerophyton circumscriptum Thallus very thick and soft, areolate, the side faces of the thick areolae often appear fluted. Thallus limited by a dark prothallus. The orange alga *Trentepohlia* shows up if the thallus of a fresh specimen is scratched. Apothecia very small, immersed, pruinose, often arranged in lines in the areolae, spores brown, 5-7 septate, clavate.

K + y, P + o.
Habitat. Locally abundant in the West on dry, sheltered, maritime, non-calcareous to acid rocks, especially under overhangs.

S. circumscriptum x5

SCHISMATOMMA Thallus crustose. Apothecia not seen in Britain. Usually shows orange when a fresh specimen is scratched, due to the phycobiont *Trentepohlia*. Often with a weak, dark prothallus.

Thallus, mauve grey, K −, P −	**S. decolorans**
Thallus pale grey, K −, P + o.	**S. niveum**
Thallus pure white, K + y, P −	**S. virgineum**

Schismatomma decolorans Thallus mauve-grey to brown-grey, thin, developing concolorous or slightly paler sorediate patches which usually cover the whole surface of mature specimens giving a leprose appearance.
K −, C −, P −.

Habitat. Locally common in the south and west on dry bark, most commonly in sheltered and shaded recesses of old rough-barked deciduous trees, often forming extensive patches.

S. decolorans x6

S. niveum Thallus pale grey often with a tinge of pink. Thicker than in the previous species. Concolorous or slightly paler punctiform soralia often spread to cover the whole thallus.
K − (or very pale yellow), C −, P + o.
Habitat. Rare, in the south in similar habitats to *S. decolorans,* especially on very old oak trees.

S. nivium x6

S. virgineum Similar to *S. niveum* but with a pure white thallus.
K + pale y, C −, P −.
Habitat. Not rare in the south-west, less common elsewhere, able to tolerate more open habitats than the previous species.

SOLENOPSORA Thallus placodioid or squamulose. Apothecia lecanorine. Spores colourless, one septate, 8 per ascus. Except in the extreme south-west only *S. candicans* of the three British species is at all common.

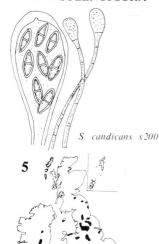

S. candicans x200

Solenopsora candicans Thallus chalky-white, placodioid, the lobes widening towards the tips, slightly convex, very pruinose. Usually fertile, apothecia with a thick thalline margin which becomes excluded. Discs black but usually heavily pruinose.
K −, P −.

Can be confused with *Buellia canescens,* but that species is sorediate, bluer-tinged, K + y and seldom fertile (except in the south).

Habitat. Locally abundant on hard calcareous rocks. In the extreme south-west on shaded rocks and soil pockets just above h.w.m. the squamulose and usually sorediate *S. vulturiensis* is common. It is often infertile, but has small brown apothecia.

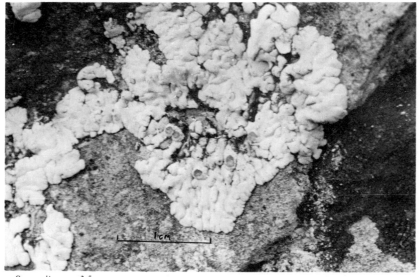

S. candicans x2.5

255

SOLORINA Thallus foliose, thin, lower surface tomentose with rhizinae. Apothecia lecideine, sunken in the surface of the thallus. Spores brown, one septate, warted in some species, up to 8 per ascus.

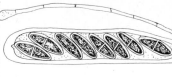

S. crocea x300

Thallus grey-brown, lower surface and medulla bright orange. K + crimson. Upland acid situations.....**S. crocea**
Thallus greenish-grey (bright green when wet), lower surface and medulla white. K −. Calcareous situations **S. saccata**

Solorina crocea Thallus brown to grey-brown, lower surface and medulla bright orange-red. Apothecia innate, large (up to 1.5cm), chestnut, flat or slightly convex. Spores brown, one septate, 8 per ascus.
Medulla K + purple.
Habitat. An arctic-alpine species of acid to slightly calcareous soils. Locally common above 900 metres in the Scottish Highlands, especially associated with areas of late snow or with permanent snow patches.

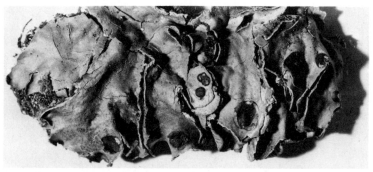

S. crocea x2

S. saccata Brownish-green to grey, bright green when wet, lower surface white or buff. Apothecia common, sunken, developing below the upper cortex which then splits to reveal the dark red-brown, flat disc of the apothecium. Spores brown, one septate, usually 4 per ascus. (A rare but rather

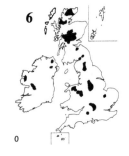

similar species, *S. bispora* has two spores per ascus.)
Medulla K −.
Habitat. Locally abundant, especially in the north, in turf, on
mosses or in crevices in hard calcareous rocks.

S. saccata x2

SPHAEROPHORUS Thallus fruticose,
bushy, branches solid, smooth not
sorediate. Apothecia borne inside the
tips of the branches. Spores brown,
simple, 8 per ascus, but the ascus breaks
down early to liberate the spores. There
are three British species.

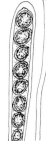

S. globosus x600

1. Main branches distinctly flattened. Medulla I −
    ....**S. melanocarpus**
    Main branches more or less terete. Medulla I − or + blue..2
2. Thallus to 6cm high, branching unequally, right up main
    stem. Medulla I + blue......................................**S. globosus**
    Thallus to 3cm high branching equally mainly from the
    base. Medulla I −..**S. fragilis**

Sphaerophorus branching patterns

S. globosus
Dichotomous, unequal

S. fragilis
Dichotomous, more
or less equal

S. melanocarpus
Palmate

257

Sphaerophorus globosus Thallus bushy, up to 6cm high, green-grey to brown, often with a pink tinge, usually brown towards the base. Many short, digitate branchlets arise in clusters right up the main stem. Apothecia develop in globose swellings in the branch tips, these swellings split open to liberate the spores.

Medulla I + blue (test in slide preparation).

Habitat. Very common in upland regions on peaty soil, rocks or mossy trees.

S. globosus x3.5

S. fragilis Thallus up to about 3cm high, bushy, forming more even and compact cushions and with fewer distinct main branches than the previous species, greenish-grey. The branchlets tend to grow all to the same height so that it often looks as though it has been mown. More doubtful specimens may be separated from S. globosus by the iodine test and the branching pattern. Only rarely fertile.

Medulla I − (test in slide preparation).

Habitat. In similar situations to S. globosus but less widely distributed.

S. fragilis x4

S. melanocarpus Thallus up to 4cm high, often decumbent, less erect than the previous species, green-grey to olive-green, lower surface often almost white. Main branches very distinct and flattened. Short rather flat branchlets arise from the edges of the main branches. Very rarely fertile in Britain.

Apothecia found on the lower side of the apices of the main branches.

Habitat. Common in N.W. Scotland, rarer elsewhere, usually amongst mosses.

S. melanocarpus x3

SQUAMARINA Thallus squamulose. Apothecia lecanorine, more or less sessile when mature. Spores colourless, simple, 8 per ascus. Closely related to *Lecanora* subgenus *Placodium*. There are two British species.

Lower surface dark..**S. crassa**
Lower surface pale..**S. lentigera**

Squamarina crassa Thallus light greenish brown to brown-green, consisting of overlapping, pruinose squamules. The pruina being most clearly seen on the margins of the squamules. Lower surface dark. Apothecia up to about 2mm. Thalline margin pronounced but may become excluded. Discs light brown to dark red-brown.

Med. P + y or P − (there are two chemical races in Britain). Habitat. A rather local species of calcareous rocks or stony calcareous soils.

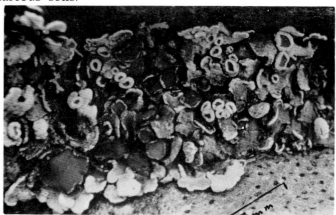

S. crassa x5

S. lentigera This is a much rarer and smaller species of highly calcareous, stony soils. It is grey-brown with a light coloured undersurface. It is especially characteristic of Breckland.
P −.

S. lentigera x2

STAUROTHELE Thallus crustose, saxicolous. Perithecia simple or compound. Spores brown (colourless when immature), 2-8 per ascus. This genus may be separated from the superficially similar *Thelidium* and *Porina* species by the presence of algal cells in the hymenium.

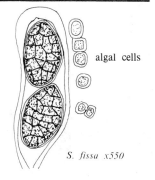

algal cells

S. fissa x550

Staurothele fissa Thallus green-grey to brown, thin or thick and areolate. Perithecia arising singly or in groups of two or three. The involucrellum dark brown and surrounded by a raised belt of the lighter thallus. Spores two per ascus, very large, brown and muriform. The paraphyses break down early in the development of the perithecia.

Habitat. Fairly common but overlooked on inundated acid rocks by streams in the north-west of Scotland, but rarer elsewhere. Often found with *Lecanora lacustris*.

S. fissa x6

STENOCYBE This species lacks a phycobiont and therefore a true thallus and is now regarded as non-lichenised. It is however included in this book due to the many references that will be found relating to it in lichen texts. Apothecia borne on the end of stalks. Spores brown, up to 3 septate, 8 per ascus.

S. pullatula x200

Fruiting bodies to 3mm high. Mainly on holly **S. septata**
Fruiting bodies to 1mm high. Mainly on alder **S. pullatula**

Stenocybe septata Apothecia dark brown, often in small groups or may be single, borne on the end of dark brown stalks. The whole being indian-club shaped and up to 3mm high, rarely taller. Spores become dark brown and 3 septate.
Habitat. Not uncommon on old shaded holly trees, exceptionally on other trees.

S. septata x16

S. pullatula Similar to the previous species but with rather wider apothecia, which together with the stalk are only about 1mm high. Spores brown becoming 3 septate.

Habitat. Occasional on alder twigs. It is most easily noticed by looking at the top edge of the twigs against the light. Often found with *Bacidia chlorococca.*

S. pullatula x16

STEREOCAULON Primary thallus usually evanescent. Secondary thallus of erect, tufted, solid, pseudopodetia, bearing flattened phyllocladia. The pseudopodetia often have cephalodia containing blue-green algae. Apothecia are not very common in Britain and are lecideine. Spores colourless, septate, 8 per ascus.

S. vesuvianum x500

May be separated from *Cladonia* as this has hollow podetia and from *Sphaeophorus* which has digitate, rounded, branchlets and simple spores in globose apothecia. *Stereocaulon* species (except *S. microscopicum*) are frequently found on metal-rich rocks when other conditions are suitable.

1. Yellowish-grey or greenish. Less than 1cm high 2
   White or grey. More than 1cm high 3
2. Greenish – grey, branch tips green-grey sorediate. K + y ....**S. pileatum**
   Yellowish-green with concolorous soralia. K − ....**[Leprocaulon] microscopicum**
3. Phyllocladia button-shaped with dark centres **S. vesuvianum**
   Phyllocladia without dark centres and/or terete............4

4. Phyllocladia flattened, incised and palmate. P −. Cephalodia rare...**S. evolutum**
Phyllocladia terete, becoming densely coralloid. P + o. Brown cephalodia common ....**S. dactylophyllum**

Stereocaulon vesuvianum Pseudopodetia white to grey, up to about 5cm high, very variable in form. It is most easily distinguished by the button – shaped phyllocladia which are narrower than the pseudopodetia and darker in the centre when mature. Cephalodia are sometimes found, very dark brown, rough and rather brain-like in appearance. This species is sometimes found fertile. Apothecia dark brown, concave at first becoming convex. Spores up to 7 septate.

K + y, P + o.

Habitat. Very common in upland regions on siliceous rocks, often forming dense mats, sometimes extending to man-made substrates.

S. vesuvianum x3.5

S. evolutum Similar to the previous species but often more spreading and branching more from the base. Many of the phyllocladia are wider than the pseudopodetia and are flattened and almost digitate. Except for the paler, digitate extremities the phyllocladia are not darker in the centre. Apothecia not common, brown with a paler margin, becoming darker and the margin excluded. Spores 3 septate. K + y, P −.

Habitat. Fairly common in acid upland regions on rocks or moss.

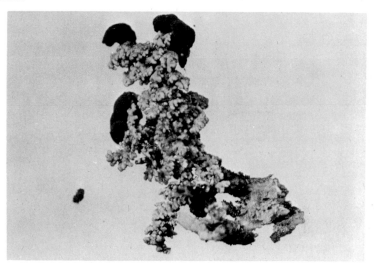

S. evolutum x5

S. dactylophyllum Pseudopodetia yellowish-white, rather stout, up to about 4cm high, often bearing brown, wrinkled clumps of cephalodia. Phyllocladia numerous, terete and becoming densely coralloid when mature. Apothecia rare, brown and convex when mature. K + y, P + o.

Habitat. Frequent on acid rocks, sometimes in lowland areas. It often forms extensive mats.

S. dactylophyllum x5

S. pileatum Pseudopodetia greenish-grey, less than 5mm high, mainly unbranched and often packed into a compact mass, giving it a crustose appearance. Phyllocladia indistinct, small, white and granular except at the apices which are grey and have green-grey soralia. Apothecia rather rare, brown and convex. Spores 3 septate. K + y, P −.

Habitat. An increasing species in man-made habitats rich in heavy metals (e.g., roadside walls and mine-spoil tips), rather rare on natural rocks.

S. pileatum x8

S. microscopicum [Leprocaulon microscopicum] Primary thallus persistent and consisting of yellowish-green granules. Pseudopodetia thin, very delicate, up to about 3mm high, unbranched or branching near the apices. Phyllocladia small, granular, very powdery and breaking down into soredia, so that superficially it appears leprose. Not known fertile or with cephalodia. K −, KC + y, P −.

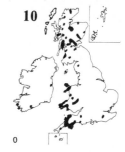

Habitat. Locally abundant, especially in the south-west, on slightly basic rocks, soil and moss, especially in somewhat shaded situations.

S . microscopicum x5

STICTA Thallus foliose. The tomentose lower surface characteristically has pale circular cyphellae, although these may be indistinct in some species. All the British species (except the rare, bright green *S. canariensis*) have blue-green algae. Not normally fertile in Britain. Apothecia lecanorine. Spores 1-3 septate, 8 per ascus. The simple reagent tests are unimportant in this genus. Some species are indicators of an "old forest" habitat.

S. fuliginosa x300

267

1. Lobe margins with dense blue-grey soredia......**S. limbata**
   Thallus isidiate, not sorediate.......................................2
2. Lobe margins with lobules and flattened isidia..**S. dufourii**
   Lobes with coralloid isidia...3
3. Lobes deeply incised so as to appear many lobed **S. sylvatica**
   Lobes little incised and few,appearing single-lobed, isidia
   more scattered ....**S. fuliginosa**

Sticta sylvatica Thallus often large (up to 20cm across), dark brown, often with greyish-brown areas, lobes deeply incised and appearing polyphyllous. Darker brown coralloid isidia and lobules are found over the surface of the lobes. Lower surface, dark brown becoming buff at the margins of the

lobes. The light rather regular cyphellae stand out against the dark lower surface. There is a strong smell of fish when damp. Habitat. Not uncommon in the west but decreasing elsewhere. Found on damp, mossy trees and rocks.

S. sylvatica   undersurface *x3*   top surface *x2*

S. fuliginosa Resembles the last species but is less incised or with an almost unlobed thallus, isidia scattered and often arising singly. Lower surface light brown. It has a strong fishy smell when damp. It is doubtfully distinct as a species from *S. sylvatica*.

Habitat. As the previous species but somewhat rarer.

S. fuliginosa x2

S. dufourii Thallus greenish–grey to brown. The lobe margins bear small lobules and flattened isidia that become laminal in mature specimens. Lower surface brown with a thin tomentum and large irregular cyphellae. It has a strong fishy smell when wet. It appears to be the same as *S. canariensis* but with blue-green algae.

Habitat. Rare in the west on mossy trees and rocks.

S. dufourii x2

S. limbata Thallus pale grey-brown to dark brown and only slightly incised. The margins of the lobes are generally incurved with dense bluish-grey granular soralia. Undersurface tan with a thick paler, tomentum, which often makes the cyphellae indistinct. There is no fishy smell.

Habitat. Fairly common in the west on mossy trees and rocks. It can tolerate more basic substrates than *S. fuliginosa* and *S. sylvatica*.

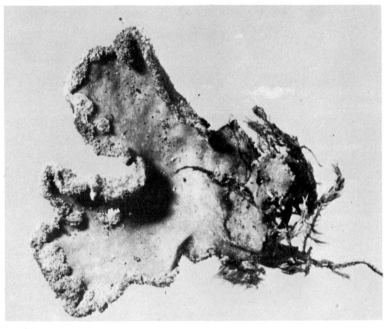

S. limbata x5

TELOSCHISTES Thallus fruticose. Greenish-orange to bright orange. Cortex K + purple. Apothecia lecanorine, spores colourless, polarilocular, 8 per ascus. Britain is at the northern end of the range of this mainly Mediterranean to sub-tropical genus.

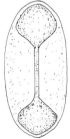

T. flavicans x1750

Teloschistes flavicans. Thallus erect or slightly pendent, green-orange to deep orange. The lobes are up to 4cm long and rather flattened and much branched, with claw shaped, long spinules. The margins bear yellowish farinose soredia which may rub off and leave pits in the cortex. Apothecia very rare in Britain (no recent records). Discs orange with a thin margin. The form found on supralittoral rocks is bright orange-yellow, more terete, glossy and less branched forming a decumbent mat. K + p.

Habitat. Formerly a widespread but now rare and a very local species of well-lit, nutrient-enriched bark and maritime rocks. Not to be collected.

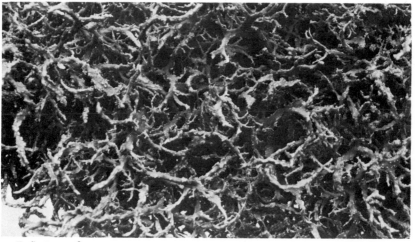

T. flavicans x5

T. chrysophthalmus Thallus greyish-orange forming much smaller tufts than the previous species. Usually very fertile with abundant spinulose apothecia. It was found on well lit nutrient-enriched twigs in S.W. England, but now appears to be extinct on mainland Britain, but it is still found in the Channel Islands.

K + p

T. chrysophthalmus x6

THAMNOLIA Thallus fruticose, consisting of simple or sparsely branched hollow tubes. Never reported with apothecia, it also lacks soredia or isidia and is presumed to be spread by fragmentation. It is found throughout the world in arctic-alpine habitats above about 2,000 feet, but down to sea level in Canada, Greenland, etc. It is especially common in these high latitudes.

Thamnolia vermicularis [s.l.] Thallus white to yellowish-white, slightly wrinkled, branches up to 5cm, narrowing slowly to a point, sometimes flattened and fluted, unbranched or slightly branched. Forms loose mats or more commonly is scattered amongst mosses and dwarf shrubs. K + y, P + y.

Habitat. Common in arctic-alpine situations, mainly above 2,000 feet (in Britain), especially in lichen-rich mature heath with dwarf shrubs.

T. vermicularis x5

THELIDIUM Thallus crustose, often endolithic or thin. Perithecia may be compound. Spores 1-3 septate, often clavate, 8 per ascus. In the field, it is difficult, to separate some species from the closely related genus *Verrucaria,* but that genus has simple spores.

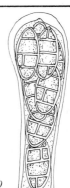

T. incavatum x400

1. Perithecia to 1mm wide, hemispherical...........**T. papulare**
    Peritheica to 0.5mm wide. More or less immersed.......2
2. Perithecia 0.25—0.4mm wide. Spores 3 septate. Soft limestone...**T. incavatum**
    Perithecia to 0.5mm wide. Spores 1 septate. Hard calcareous rocks..**T. decipiens**

Thelidium papulare Thallus light grey to purplish-grey, thin and leprose, sometimes cracked. Perithecia about 1mm diam, hemispherical with a smooth depression in the centre around the ostiole. Spores 3 septate or slightly muriform.
Habitat. An infrequent species of damp calcareous rocks, particularly in the west.

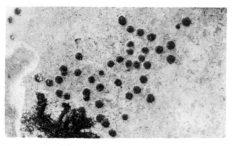

T. papulare x5

x35

T. incavatum Thallus white or pale grey, thin or endolithic. Perithecia small, about 0.25-0.4mm, more or less immersed with only the ostiole showing, leaving pits when the perithecia falls out. Spores 3 septate or slightly muriform.

Habitat. An infrequent species of soft limestone. More southerly than *T. papulare.*

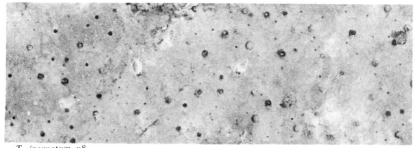

T. incavatum x8

T. decipiens Thallus white or pale grey or endolithic. Perithecia immersed, about 0.5mm diam. with a prominent ostiole. The perithecia leave pits when they fall out. Spores 1 septate, clavate.

Habitat. A frequent species of hard calcareous rocks.

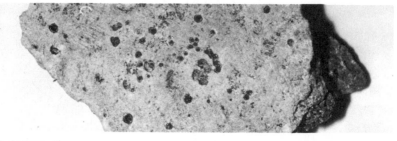

T. decipiens x6

THELOTREMA Thallus crustose. Ascocarps with a detached, enclosing thalline margin and a fused proper margin, giving it a double appearance. Spores colourless or brown, multiseptate or muriform, up to 8 per ascus. This is mainly a tropical genus. (Note: *Ocellularia* and *Leptotrema* are treated as synonyms.)

T. lepadinum x250

Thelotrema lepadinum Thallus creamy-white to grey, thin, or thick and ridged. Apothecia with a large central opening, mature fruits shaped like a ring doughnut. The proper margin is visible inside the thalline margin, giving the apothecium the appearance of a barnacle. Spores colourless, elongate fusiform with transverse septa.

Habitat. Common in sheltered situations in unpolluted areas, mainly on deciduous trees. It is an "old-forest" species.

T. lepadinum x10

TOMASELLIA Thallus crustose, thin or endophloeoedal. Ascocarps flask-shaped and grouped together in a cushion-like stroma, only separated from each other by thin walls. Spores colourless, up to 3 septate, 8 per ascus. There is some doubt that this genus is really lichenized.

T. gelatinosa x500

Tomasellia gelatinosa Thallus buffish-grey or not apparent. Perithecia grouped together in a rather flat, black, compound fruit, up to several millimetres across. The ostioles are visible at the top of each perithecium in the group. Spores colourless or pale brown up to 3 septate.

Habitat. Rather common on smooth–barked trees (almost exclusively *Corylus*) especially in the west. (Microscopic examination is essential to separate this species from certain similar looking fungi.)

T. gelatinosa x15

TONINIA Thallus squamulose (usually with deep "roots"). The commonest British species are found in basic sites. Apothecia lecideine, black, large and globose. Spores colourless, 1-3 septate, 8 per ascus.

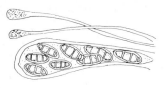

T. aromatica x350

Squamules warted and contorted, not pruinose. Spores 3 septate ....**T. aromatica**

Squamules smooth, involute, pruinose. Spores 1 septate ....**T. coeruleonigricans**

Toninia aromatica Thallus light to dark grey. Squamules warted and contorted, appearing crustose from above. Apothecia usually numerous, black, plane to convex, up to 3mm across, often angular in shape. Spores 3 septate. Habitat. Common on calcareous rocks and mortar.

T. aromatica x6

T. coeruleonigricans Thallus pale grey to brown-grey, distinctly pruinose. The squamules large, smooth and involute. Apothecia black, plane to convex, up to 5mm or more across, angular in outline. The young apothecia are pruinose with a thick black margin. Spores 1 septate. Habitat. A locally abundant species of calcareous soils, crevices in limestone rock and sand dunes.

T. coeruleonigricans x5

UMBILICARIA Thallus foliose, attached only at one central point (umbilicate), often found on detached boulders. Apothecia lecideine or gyrose. Spores colourless or brown, simple or muriform. Members of this genus have been eaten ("rock tripe") and used as a survival food in the arctic. One species,

U. pustulata x350

U. esculenta, is eaten as a delicacy in Japan. The British species are thin, papery and brittle when dry, becoming greenish or brownish and pliable when wet.

1. Thallus pruinose, brown and pustulate or grey often with stiff marginal fibrils..2
   Thallus mid to dark brown, not pruinose, not pustulate or with marginal fibrils..3
2. Thallus greenish – brown, coarsely pustulate. Medulla C + red..**[Lasallia] pustulata**
   Thallus pale grey with many stiff, dark fibrils on the lobe margins. Medulla C –...................................**U. cylindrica**
3. Thallus becoming tesselated. Margins perforated..............
   .... **U. torrefacta**
   Thallus smooth, margins entire or lobulate....................4
4. Lobes dark brown, distorted to appear multilobed, thin and papery, undersurface lacks rhizinae...............**U. polyphylla**
   Lobes copper brown, robust and rounder, undersurface a dense, felt-like mass of black rhizinae ....**U. polyrrihiza**

Umbilicaria pustulata [Lasallia pustulata]
Thallus mid to dark brown when dry. The surface is covered in large swollen pustules, which, in the centre of the thallus are covered in a heavy pruina. Not commonly found fertile, apothecia lecideine, smooth, black, superficial, not gyrose. The margins become tattered and often have numerous dark brown coralloid isidia. The undersurface of the thallus is dark brown and reticulate, with depressions that correspond to the swellings on the upper surface. There are no rhizinae. This species has been used in dyeing.

Medulla C + r, KC + r.

Habitat. Common on nutrient-enriched rocks in upland situations, where it may form extensive colonies. Seldom found growing with *U. polyphylla* and *U. polyrrhiza* which prefer more acid habitats.

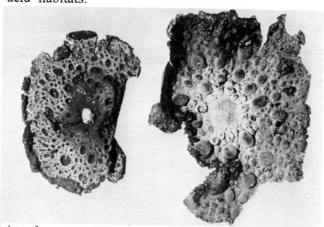

U. pustulata x2

U. torrefacta Thallus dark brown, slightly shiny, the margins irregular, perforated and becoming lace-like. In well developed specimens the surface becomes tesselated and almost appears to be covered in small lobules. Undersurface lighter brown with some or many coarse rhizinae and radiating

279

trabecula. Apothecia black and gyrose. Spores colourless. C + r, KC + r.

Habitat. Locally abundant on hard siliceous rocks in mainly upland regions.

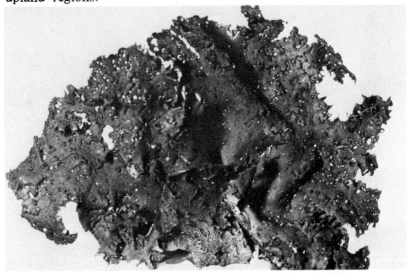

U. torrefacta x3

U. cylindrica Thallus pale to dark grey, very pruinose. The margins of the lobes curl upwards and are usually fringed with stiff dark fibrils. Undersurface buff or grey, pruinose, with few or many rhizinae and often trabeculate. Frequently fertile with gyrose, black, superficial apothecia. Spores colourless, simple.

Reactions negative.

Habitat. Locally abundant on rocks mainly in upland regions, especially in the Scottish Highlands, Lake District, Snowdonia and western Ireland.

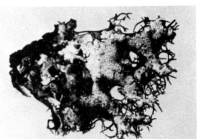

U. cylindrica x2

U. polyrrhiza Thallus deep copper to brown, smooth, often almost shiny and lacking pruina, the lobes often becoming much distorted and imbricate, the edges turning down and breaking up into small lobules. Undersurface black and rather granular with black forked rhizinae forming a dense felt-like mass that protrudes beyond the edges of the lobes. Apothecia very rare, black, lecideine, superficial, not gyrose but with radiating ridges and no margin. Spores colourless, simple.
Medulla C + r, KC + r.
Habitat. Not uncommon on hard siliceous rocks and exposed boulders in upland regions.

6

0   **C**

U. polyrrhiza x2

U. polyphylla Thallus dark brown to almost black, smooth and slightly shiny, not pruinose, much contorted so as to appear multilobed, extremely brittle and thin, difficult to remove intact from the substrate. Undersurface black, more or less smooth and differs from the previous species by the complete lack of rhizinae. Apothecia extremely rare.
Medulla C + r, KC + r.

5

0

Habitat. Not uncommon on hard smooth siliceous rocks in upland areas. Often found growing with *U. polyrrhiza*.

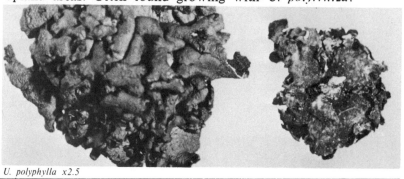

U. polyphylla x2.5

USNEA Thallus fruticose, much branched, bushy, erect, pendent or trailing, often with a distinct base, terete with a tough central core (this is usually visible if the cortex is broken or the thallus stretched). Apothecia lecanorine, sub-terminal. Spores colourless, simple, 8 per ascus. This genus is used in

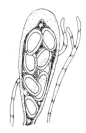

U. florida x900

Scandinavia to produce a powerful antibiotic, and it has had many uses in the past. These include the hair powder, "cyprus powder", for uterine complaints, to arrest haemorrhages, and even as a source of glucose. The cortex KC + y (usnic acid) reaction and the medulla reactions are useful in separating some species.

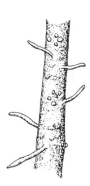

Side branch
constricted at junction
with main branch

Soredia and isidia
U. subfloridana

Spines and warts
U. florida

Soredia

U. fulvoreagens

1. Thallus long with tight constrictions (like a string of sausages). No persistent base. No soralia. Medulla P + red, K −. (West) ....U. **articulata**
   Thallus not inflated, not strongly sausage-shaped, having a persistent base.. Reactions various 2

2. Thallus yellow-green to grey-green 3
   Thallus dull reddish or brownish. Medulla K + y, P + o
   .... U. **rubiginea**

3. Sorediate and/or isidiate..4
   Not sorediate or isidiate but with small pointed branchlets, (usually in fruit with fringed margins). Medulla K + y, P + o ....U. **florida**

4. Concave patches of soralia and isidia, bushy bottle-brush appearance, holdfast blackened. Medulla K + y to r, P + o (common)..,........U. **subfloridana**
   Having either soralia or isidia, not both 5

5. Sorediate 6
   Isidiate...7

6. Soralia superficial, branches long and fine .U. **glabrescens**
   Abundant granular soredia in eroded pits. Apical branches recurved .... U. **fulvoreagens**

7. Thallus soft and flexible even when dry, yellowish-green, pendent, branchlets constricted at junctions. Holdfast not blackened. Medulla K + y ....U. **fragilescens**
   Thallus not soft and flexible when dry, often more grey-green 8

8. Cortex and/or medulla K + yellow to red 9
   Medulla K− 10

9. Thallus long and pendent, consisting of a few long interwoven branches with short secondary branches, holdfast often densely isidiate......................................U. **filipendula**
   Thallus bushy, more or less erect.Isidia scattered U. **inflata**

10. Main branches smooth but with long isidia, often yellowish-green, flexible when wet........................U. **hirta**
    Main branches tuberculate. Isidia short and scattered (or absent), stiff even when wet. Central axis often pink ....U. **ceratina**

Usnea articulata Thallus grey-green (yellow-green when dry in an herbarium), no distinct base, up to 1 metre or more in length. Main branches up to 5mm or more in diameter, generally smooth but sometimes fluted and with delicate spinulose branchlets. The branches are sharply constricted

10

down to the central core, to give the appearance of a string of sausages. Not known fertile in Britain.

Medulla Pd + r, K −, KC −. (There are many other chemical races which are not found in Britain.)

Habitat. A locally common species in the extreme south and west where it festoons well-lit hedges, trees and more rarely dunes and rocks. One of the most SO_2 pollution sensitive species, formerly widespread in England, it even used to grow near London. It still grows as far north as the Isle of Man.

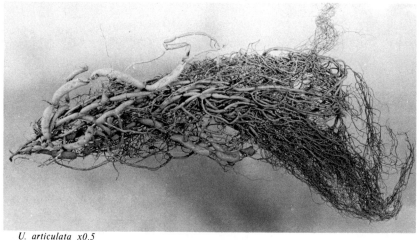

U. articulata x0.5

U. florida Thallus yellow-green, bushy, more or less erect or pendent. The base is persistent and generally blackened. The main branches are coarse with warts and small spines and a stout central axis. Both the main and secondary branches have many pointed branchlets, these are not attenuated at

9

0

their junction with the main stems. Almost always found fertile with large (up to 1cm) fawn-coloured discocarps which are surrounded by radial spinulose branchlets. These large rayed discocarps form a particularly distinctive feature, but are found in a number of other species. It was used in the nineteenth century for the production of alcohol.

Medulla K + deep y, P + orange-red.

Habitat. Common on well-lit twigs and branches especially in old woods and caves. It also occurs on fence posts. Found in the south and west it becomes rarer northward and may now not occur north of Anglesey.

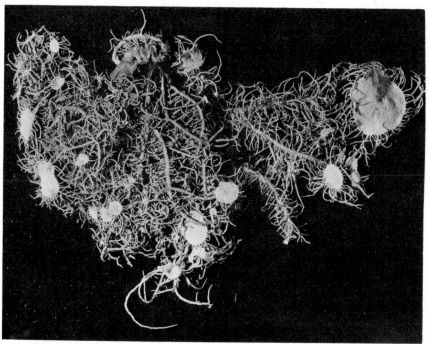

U. florida x2

U. subfloridana Thallus yellow-green to grey-green, erect and bushy or sometimes slightly pendent, it is distinctly blackened near the coarse, persistent holdfast. It differs from *U. florida* primarily in the concave patches of soredia and isidia and the lack of wart-like nodules. Much less commonly

285

fertile than *U. florida* but with similar although much smaller apothecia.

Medulla K + y or o, P + y to orange-red (there are a number of chemical races).

Habitat. By far the most common and widespread of the British *Usnea* species. It grows on trees, fences and more rarely on rock, often on thicker branches and boles of trees, and often in more open situations than *U. florida*. It is the most tolerant species of this genus in Britain to air pollution, but it has largely disappeared from the Midlands.

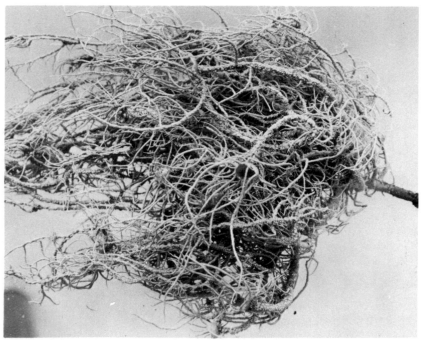

U. subfloridana x4

U. glabrescens This species resembles *U. subfloridana* except for the abundance of superficial soralia and a complete lack of isidia. Together with longer, finer branchlets. It is less common than the previous species of which it represents a type characteristic of more humid sites and is only very doubtfully distinct from it.

U. fulvoreagens Thallus grey-green, tufted, coarse, subpendent, small (usually much less than 5cm), the base is often blackened. The branchlets rather sparse, long and thin and characteristically with the tips conspicuously bent over towards the substrate. The branches split and give  rise to granular soredia, which may almost cover the branches. There are no isidia.

Medulla K + y, P + o.

Habitat. A very local species of the extreme south and west of Britain. It has frequently been wrongly interpreted.

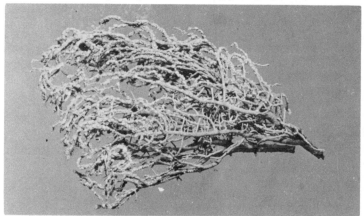

U. fulvoreagens x4

U. fragilescens Thallus pale yellowish green or straw coloured, more or less pendulous, up to about 10cm long, soft and flexible even when dry, central axis not stout. Base persistent and not blackened. Branchlets constricted at the junction with the main branches. Groups of small pointed isidia are  scattered over the warted branches. These isidia resemble those of *U. subfloridana*, but there are no soredia.

Medulla K + y, P + o.

Habitat. Common on trees and fence posts in the north and west of Britain, becoming common northwards.

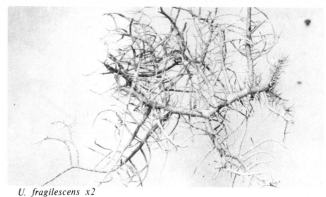

U. fragilescens x2

U. inflata *(U. intexta, U. subpectinata)*
Thallus dull greyish-green often with a waxy blue tinge, coarse, more or less tufted or subpendent, up to about 5cm long. Base persistent and not blackened. Branches rather stout, markedly constricted where they join the main branches. There are also slight

constrictions at intervals along the branches. The cortex often splits open at these points exposing the relatively stout central axis. Small isidia (which sometimes erode) are scattered over the branches, either in groups or singly.

Medulla K + y/o, P + y/o to red (2 chemical races).

Habitat. Not uncommon in rather more shaded situations than most species in this genus. Found on trees and rocks in the south and west, extending into western Scotland, where it is not rare.

U. inflata x2

U. filipendula Thallus rather dark grey-green, subpendent or trailing, consisting of a few, long, straggling, intertwined, main branches and many short branches, diverging sharply from the main branch. Near the holdfast dense isidia are often found on the top of coarse warts. These isidia are also found on the other branches.
Medulla K + y to red, P + o.
Habitat. Not uncommon in upland woods (especially on conifers) in the north of Britain.

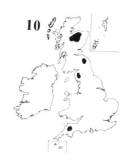

U. filipendula x3

U. hirta Thallus dark green-grey, often almost olive-green, bushy or pendent, up to about 4cm high. Very soft and flexible when wet, axis narrow, base persistent and rarely blackened. The main branches and especially the tips covered in long thin isidia, no soredia. Lateral branches constricted where they join the main stems.
Cortex KC + y, medulla K-, P −.
Habitat. Locally abundant species of conifers and fences, often on exposed sites, especially in the Scottish Highlands. Prefers more acid sites than the other British species, except for *U. filipendula.*

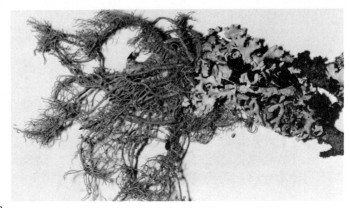

U. hirta x2

U. ceratina Thallus grey-green, coarsely pendent or subpendent, up to 1 metre long. Consists of relatively few main branches with some sub-branches and a number of long fibrils which grow out at right angles to the main stem. Branches constricted where they join the main stem, There are also constrictions at intervals along the main branches, showing as paler annular rings. Central axis usually pink (stretch plant to break the cortex). The branches are smooth at first but usually develop small isidia.

Medulla K −, KC −, P −, CK + deep yellow.

Habitat. Locally abundant on well-lit trees in the south, not found in the north. It is now less widespread due to the increase in air pollution.

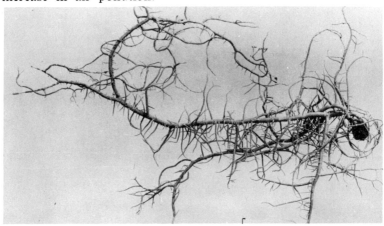

U. ceratina x1

U. rubiginea [U. rubicunda] Thallus distinctive brownish-red or greyish-red, coarse, tufted or subpendent, usually less than 12cm long. Base persistent and not blackened. Side branches rather sparse and at right angles to the main stem, constricted at the junction and with long attenuated tips. The stems warted and with clusters of isidia which may cover the base of the stems these erode and become sorediate. The main axis is stout. Take care not to confuse the red colour found in other species due to poor condition and the decomposition of salazinic acid. Medulla K + y, P + y.

Habitat. Locally abundant on trees in unpolluted regions in the south and west, becoming rarer northwards.

U. rubiginea x3

VERRUCARIA Except for one very rare species of calcareous soil *(V. psammophila)*, all the British species are saxicolous, being found in a wide range of habitats, from well below the high tide mark to mountain summits. Thallus crustose. Perithecia either immersed or prominent, single or sometimes grouped together. Spores colourless, simple, 8 per ascus.

V. maura x500

291

1. Found near or below high-water mark or in freshwater streams...2
   Found on basic rock, not necessarily near water 6
2. Maritime 3
   In or very near freshwater streams 5
3. Thallus thick and regularly cracked. Near high-water mark
   ....**V. maura**
   Thallus green to brown-green; if brown-black, smooth and
   rather thin. Usually below h.w.m. 4
4a. Thallus green with black ridges and prominent black
   perithecia...**V. striatula**
   b. Thallus green, not ridged, thick and smooth, perithecia in-
   nate when wet ....**V. mucosa**
   c. Thallus green-brown to dark brown, smooth, perithecia
   small but prominent even when wet ....**V. microspora**
5. Thallus brown or dark green, with prominent perithecia.
   Spores almost globose (c.6 x 8 μm) ....**V. aquatilis**
   Thallus green to brown-green, containing black granules,
   perithecia immersed. Spores ellipsoid (c.10 x 20 μm)
   ....**V. elaeomelaena**
6. Thallus green to chocolate-brown 7
   Thallus white or grey..9
7. Thallus dark brown, finely cracked, often with a black
   prothallus. Perithecia to 0.5mm ....**V. nigrescens**
   Thallus green to green-brown, wide cracks (like dried mud).
   Perithecia to almost 1mm but often absent....................8
8. Without soredia ....**V. viridula**
   Concolorous or paler soredia along edges of cracks
   ....**V. viridula** f. **tectorum**
9. Thallus pale leaden—grey, with rather regular areolae
   separated into small islets by the black prothallus**V. glaucina**
   Thallus white, smooth or powdery 10
10. Thallus smooth or rarely evanescent. Perithecia sunken,
   about 0.25mm wide. On hard limestone
   ....**V. sphinctrina**
   Thallus evanescent or sometimes powdery. Perithecia about
   1mm wide or more..11
11. Perithecia to 1mm wide, leaving empty pits when they fall
   out ....**V. muralis**

Perithecia to 1.5mm often leaving black remains in pits
....**V. hochstetteri**

MARITIME

Verrucaria maura Thallus black and thick and has been confused with dried oil washed ashore. Under a lens the thallus is cracked into rather rectangular areolae, with numerous conical perithecia with distinct ostioles. These features are less noticeable when the thallus is wet.

Habitat. Very common on rocky coasts, found from below, to some distance above the h.w.m. It usually forms the main constituent of the upper part of the black zone found on coastal rocks.

V. maura x8

V. microspora Thallus green-brown to dark brown-black, smooth or only slightly cracked. Perithecia dark and prominent, very small (less than 0.5mm diam).

Habitat. Common on most rocky coasts but generally not very abundant, it is only found below h.w.m..

V. microspora x6

V. mucosa Thallus green to dark olive-green, thick, and not, or only slightly irregularly cracked, often limited by a white prothallus. Perithecia black, immersed but becoming more prominent when dry, very small (less than 0.5mm diam).

Habitat. Common and often very abundant in similar habitats to *V. microspora*.

V. mucosa x5

V. striatula Thallus green to dark green, smooth and continuous. Elevated black ridges that are sometimes radial or in lines are found especially on specimens from exposed coasts. This feature distinguishes this species from the others treated here. Perithecia very prominent, black, usually with a large irregular ostiole.

Habitat. Common on hard rocks at about h.w.m.

V. striatula x8

AQUATIC (freshwater)

V. aquatilis Thallus brown to dark green, thin but continuous. Many rather prominent black perithecia are scattered over the surface. Spores 6-8 × 4-7μm. Habitat. The commonest of the freshwater *Verrucaria* species. It is found in clear streams, mainly in upland regions.

V. aquatilis x12

V. elaeomelaena Thallus green to brown-green often with a wide, white or black prothallus. The perithecia are immersed with only the ostioles visible at the surface. Small dark granules imbedded in the thallus are usually present. It has a rather similar appearance to *V. mucosa*. Spores 16-28 × 6-15μm.

Habitat. Found in similar habitats to the previous species, but less common. It may be confused with the rarer *V. kernstockii*, which has similar, but generally larger black granules in the thallus, its spores are only 8-12 × 6-8μm.

V. elaeomelaena x6

ROCKS and WALLS
(not necessarily aquatic or maritime)

V. nigrescens Thallus chocolate-brown, usually thick and regularly cracked with a black prothallus, rarely thin and scurfy. Perithecia small (less than 0.5mm), frequently in groups immersed in the thallus and easily overlooked, frequently in groups.
Habitat. An exceedingly common species of calcareous rocks, walls, tombstones, etc., throughout the British Isles.

V. nigrescens x3

V. viridula Thallus green to dark green-brown, thick and cracked like dried mud (*V. nigrescens* has much narrower cracks). Perithecia mainly compound and immersed, up to almost 1mm diam. Form *tectorum* differs in the concolorous or slightly lighter soralia found along the edges of the cracks.

Habitat. Common on basic rocks, including brick. May be confused with *Acarospora* species, but these are found on siliceous rocks, have several hundred spores per ascus, and have larger areoles.

V. viridula x10

V. muralis Thallus white and powdery but often evanescent. Apothecia black, prominent, simple, with a distinct ostiole, up to 1mm diam, but usually smaller. The apothecia fall out and leave empty cavities in the substrate.

Habitat. Exceedingly common on rather soft calcareous rocks, walls and mortar.

V. hochstetteri is rather similar but with slightly larger apothecia, up to 1.5mm, the lower half of the perithecium often remains in the cavity and does not fall out. The thallus is a brillant white and it is usually found on harder rocks.

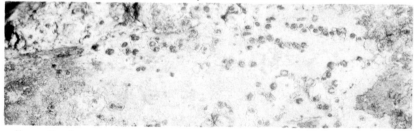

V. muralis x8

V. sphinctrina Thallus brilliant white, thin, smooth, or more rarely evanescent, usually with a dark, narrow prothallus. The surface crowded with many small (about 0.25mm), immersed perithecia. These leave empty pits in the substrate when they die.

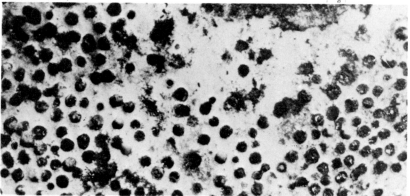

V. sphinctrina x10

V. glaucina Thallus pale leaden-grey, thick and cracked. The surface of the thallus showing a black, net-like prothallus. Perithecia under 0.25mm diam.

Habitat. Fairly common and widespread, usually forming small islets amongst other species. Found on basic rocks, walls and mortar.

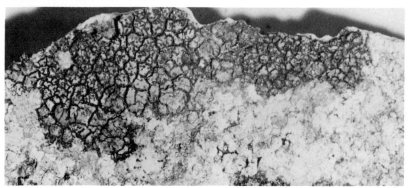

V. glaucina x6

XANTHORIA Thallus foliose, orange.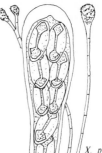
Apothecia lecanorine. Spores colourless,
polarilocular, 8 per ascus. They are
characteristically found on nutrient-rich
sites. In their colour and the K +
crimson reaction they resemble
Caloplaca species, they differ in being
foliose and it is possible to peel them off

X. parietina x600

the substrate. The yellow colour led to them being tried as a
cure for jaundice. A yellow and a crimson dye have been
extracted from these species.

Xanthoria parietina Thallus greenish-grey
in shade to bright orange where exposed,
forming orbicular patches in which, in
old specimens, the centre often dies out.
Lobes long (narrow in very exposed
situations, e.g. the seashore), wrinkled,
imbricate, the edges of the lobes often
turned up. Undersurface almost white

with a few light coloured rhizinae. Apothecia usually abundant
towards the centre of the thallus, disc orange with a paler
margin that becomes crenulate.
K + crimson.
Habitat. Very common on nutrient-rich trees, rocks, and walls,
especially bird-perching sites, farms, etc. This is one of the most
resistant foliose species to air pollution.

X. parientina x3

X. aureola Thallus similar to the previous species, often deeper orange with more contorted lobes, which become densely covered in coralloid wart-like isidia. Apothecia are also similar but much less abundant and often entirely absent.
K + crimson.

Habitat. Common on similar habitats to *X. parietina* but only exceptionally found on trees. Rarer in the west than the east of Britain.

X. aureola x2

X. elegans Thallus bright orange-red, closely adpressed, with narrow (up to 1mm wide) convex lobes, usually forming a neat orbicular patch. Apothecia usually present, orange-red with crenulate margins.
K + crimson.

Habitat. Frequent in nutrient-rich rocks in mountain and upland areas, but currently extending its range to concrete and slate in more lowland areas.

X. elegans x4

X. polycarpa Thallus greenish-grey to yellow-orange, orbicular, up to 2cm across. Marginal lobes incised and often almost obscured by the numerous crowded and stalked apothecia. These have orange discs and thick pale margins that become somewhat crenulate. K + crimson.

Habitat. Common on nutrient-rich trees, especially the angles of twigs, but also found on fences and dead trees.

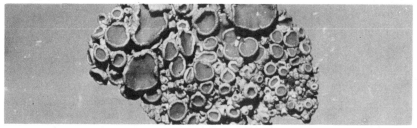

X. polycarpa x5

X. candelaria Thallus yellow-orange, consisting of a mass of ascending, crenulate lobes, up to 3mm wide and high. The undersurface white with yellow granular soralia at the tips. Not usually fertile. Apothecia orange with a contorted margin. This species was used in Scandinavia to dye church candles yellow.

K + crimson. This reaction and the more orange-yellow help separate this species from the superficially similar *Candelaria concolor*.

Habitat. Common on nutrient-enriched (usually deciduous) trees, fences and especially rocks.

X. candelaria x10

XYLOGRAPHA Thallus crustose, often endolignate. Apothecia lecideine becoming lirellate when mature. Spores colourless, simple, 8 per ascus.

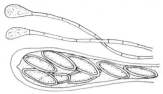

X. abietina x400

Xylographa abietina Thallus immersed or thin, white to greenish-grey. Apothecia brown and oval when young, with a thin margin and a roughened disc. They become black and lirellate, following the grain of the wood. The margins are often excluded in mature apothecia. Reactions negative.

Habitat. Locally common on decorticated wood and tree stumps in the north of Britain.

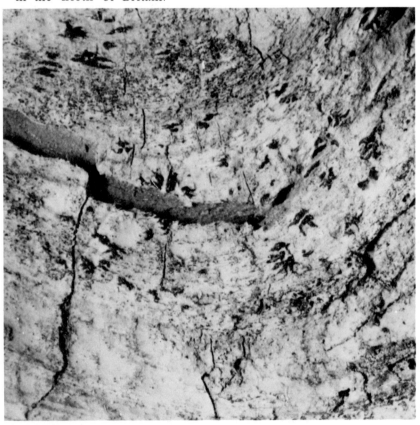

X. abietina x10

A Typical acid-heathland community, including *Cladonia impexa, C. furcata, C. fimbriata, G. chlorophaea* and *Hypogymnia physodes*.

Selected Bibliography

ALVIN K.L. *The Observer's Book of Lichens* (1977) Warne.
An inexpensive book giving good colour and monochrome illustrations.

DAHL E. and KROG H. *Macrolichens* (1973) Universitets-forlaget.
Key and illustration to Scandinavian macrolichens but still of great use in Britain.

DOBSON F. S. *Common British Lichens* (1979) Jarrold.
Text and over 40 colour illustrations in an inexpensive format.

DUNCAN U.K. *Introduction to British Lichens* (1970).
Distributed by The Richmond Publishing Co. Ltd.
The standard work on the identification of British lichens.

HALE Mason E. *The Biology of Lichens* (1974) Ed. Arnold
Covers many aspects of the biology of lichens.

HAWKSWORTH D.L. & ROSE F. *Lichens as Pollution Monitors* (1976) Ed. Arnold.
An indispensable book for anyone interested in the effects of pollution on British lichens.

HAWKSWORTH D.L. and SEAWARD M.R.D. *Lichenology in the British Isles 1568 – 1975* (1977) Richmond Publishing
A history of lichenology in Britain and a very comprehensive bibliography.

SMITH A. L. *Lichens* (1921) C.U.P. (reprinted with new introduction 1975) The Richmond Publishing Co. Ltd.
Although now somewhat dated it contains much information and references that cannot be found elsewhere.

All the above books (or any other Botanical titles) may be obtained directly from:

Retail Book Sales Dept, The Richmond Publishing Co. Ltd. Orchard Road, Richmond, Surrey, England.

GLOSSARY

Acid rocks. Siliceous, not reacting to hydrochloric acid.

Adpressed. Flat and close to the substrate.

Agg. Aggregate, several species combined.

Anastomose. Net-like.

Apical. At the tip.

Apothecium(a). Disc shaped or elongate fruit-containing asci.

Arachnoid. Fine, web-like.

Arctic-alpine. Lacking nutrients, usually Erica or Calluna dominated.

Areola(ae). Islands formed by cracks in the thallus.

Arthonioid. Type of fruiting body without a true margin. See p. XXIII.

Ascospore. See spore.

Ascus(i). Bag shaped structures containing the spores.

Atranorin. A substance produced by many lichens giving a K + yellow reaction

Attenuated. Drawn out to a fine point or constricted.

Axil. Junction of a branch.

Basidiomycete. Fungus bearing the spores on a basidium and not producing them in an ascus.

Bullate. Ridged and blister-like.

Calcareous. Chalky, alkaline, rocks or soil.

Caniculate. Channeled, trough-shaped.

Capitate. Terminating a lobe or branch.

Capitulum. Spore-bearing area at the apex of some stalked apothecia.

Carbonaceous. Hard, black.

Chemotype. Races of a species that differ only in their chemical constituents.

Chromatography A sensitive method for determining the chemical constituents.

Cephalodium(a). Area of thallus in a lichen; normally with a green alga, that differs in containing a blue-green alga; often forming outgrowths.

Cilia. Long hair-like structures on the lobe ends or margins.

Clavate. Club-shaped, wider at one end.

Concolorous. The same colour.

Confluent. Growing together to cover the surface.

Conidia. Spores produced asexually from fungal cells.

Convex. Curved upwards to the centre.

Convoluted. Twisted and contorted.

Coralloid. Pencil-like or branched like coral.

Cortex. The outer layers of the thallus, consisting of fungal hyphae.

Corticate. Having a cortex.

Corticolous. Growing on bark.

Crenulate. More or less regularly notched.

Crustose. Thallus type. See p. XIX.

Cyphella(ae). Regular holes though the cortex.

Decorticate. Areas where the cortex has degenerated.

Decumbent. Spreading over the ground not upright (except at the tips).

Delimited. Having clearly defined borders.

Dentate. Tooth-like.

Determinate. Having a clear edge.

Dichotomous. Divided in two, forked.

Digitate. Having finger-like projections.

Disc. The central upper surface inside the margins of the apothecium.

Discocarps. Disc-shaped fruiting bodies.

Discrete. In separate patches.

Dorsiventral. Upper and lower surfaces differing, sometimes used to mean vertically compressed.

Effuse. Spread thinly.

Endolignate. Thallus growing within wood.

Endolithic. Thallus growing inside the rock.

Endophloeodal. The thallus growing within bark.

Entire. Complete, continuous.

Epidermis. Outer cell layer of young twigs and leaves.

Epithecium. The upper layer of the thecium above the asci, formed by the tips of the paraphyses.

Ericaceous. Predominantly on heathers and heaths.

Erumpent. Busting through the cortex or substrate.

Evanescent. Disappearing early.

Exciple. Exipulum. Tissue surrounding the thecium and evident as the proper margin.

Excluded. Eliminated.

Farinose. Flour-like.

Fibrils. Stout hair-like growths or secondary, often perpendicular, branchlets.

Filamentous. Thallus type. See p. XVII.

Fimbriate. Fringed.

Fissural. Growing in splits in the cortex.

Foliose. Leaf-like. See p. XX.

Foveolate. Pitted.

Fusiform. Long, thin and pointed at each end, spindle-shaped.

Glaucous. Pale waxy, blue-grey.

Globose. More or less spherical.

Gyrose. Having a serpentine, infolded margin or raised sterile tissue within the disc.

Hapters. Small sucker-like outgrowths that attach the lichen to the substrate.

Herbarium. Storage place for botanic specimens.

h.w.m. high-water mark.

Holdfast. Root-like structure fixing certain lichens to the substrate.

Homoiomerous. Thallus more or less unstructured, not with an algal layer.

Hymenium. The area of a fruit containing the asci and paraphyses.

Hypha(ae). Fungal filaments.

Hypothallus. Dark, spongy, felted undersurface of *Pannaria* and *Parmeliella* species.

Hypothecium. The layer below the thecium.

Imbricate. Overlapping like roof tiles.

Immarginate. Lacking a clearly defined margin.

Immersed. Fruiting bodies contained within the thickness of the thallus.

Incised. Cut.

Innate. See immersed.

Involucrellum. The external cover to some perithecia.

Isidium(a). A detachable growth on the thallus surrounded by the cortex. See p. XL.

Isolichenin. A starch-like substance produced by some lichens.

Laminal. Towards the centre of the lobe, not on the edges.

Lateral branches. Secondary branches.

Lax. Loose and flexible.

Lecanorine. Apothecium having a thalline margin. See p. XXII.

Lecideine. Apothecium without a thalline margin. See p. XXII.

Lenticular. Lens-shaped.

Leprose. Thallus consisting of a more or less diffuse powdery mass. See p. XVIII.

Lignicolous. Growing on exposed or cut wood, not on living bark.

Lirella(ae). Elongate fruit, usually with a carbonaceous margin. See p. XXII

Lobate. Having lobes.

Lobules. Small secondary lobes.

Loculate. With cavities.

Maculate. Blotched and patchy.

Margin. See p. XXII.

Maritime. Under the influence of sea-spray, but not submerged.

Mazaedium. A loose mass of spores, etc, formed when the asci break down simultaneously.

Medulla. The inner part of the thallus lacking algae, usually of loosely packed fungal hyphae.

Monophyllus. Thallus consisting of only one lobe.

Mosaic. Forming a community growing together but with each thallus clearly defined.

Multiseptate. Having a number of transverse septa. See p. XVII.

Muriform. Having longitudinal and transverse septa. See p. XVII.

Musicolous. Growing on moss.

Mycobiont. The fungal partner.

Nutrient-rich. Substrate rich in basic compounds, e.g. enriched by bird droppings, fertilizer, etc.

Obtuse. Branching at a wide angle, or with rounded ends.

Oceanic. Petaining to the milder, damper west coast.

"Old Forest". Species characteristic of a forest with a long continuity of mature trees.

Orbiculate. Circular in outline.

Ostiole. The opening at the top of a perithecium.

Ovate. Egg-shaped.

Palmate. Like the palm of the hand.

Papillate. Small wart or finger-like projections.

Paraphysis(es). Sterile filaments growing between the asci.

Pendent. Hanging down.

Perithecium(a). Flask-shaped fruiting body. See p. XXIII.

Phycobiont. Algal partner.

Phyllocladia. Small leaf-like lobes.

Placodioid. Crustose with lobed margins. See p. XIX.

Plane. Flat.

Podetium(a). Terete stalks arising from a sometimes evanescent, granular or squamulose, primary thallus. See p. XXI.

Polarilocular. Spore type having a very wide septum. See p. XVII.

Polyphyllous. Many lobed.

Proper margin. The margin of the disc containing fungal, but not algal cells, often concolorous with the disc

Prostrate. Close to the ground, not erect.

Prothallus. Area around the edge of a crustose thallus that does not contain algal cells.

Pruina. A fine white superficial powder, like the bloom on the plum.

Pseudo-. False.

Pseudocyphella(ae). Pale patches, dots and lines where the cortex is thin or absent, permiting gaseous exchange.

Punctiform. Small and sharply limited.

Pustulate. With blister-like areas.

Pycnidiospore. An asexual spore produced in a pycnidium.

Pycnidium(a). A body on the thallus that produces pycnidiospores.

Reticulate. Net-like, usually with paler lines.

Revolute. Turned down, usually at the apex.

Rhizina(ae). Root-like outgrowth of fungal filaments.

Saxicolous. Growing on rock.

Scabrid. Rough and scurfy.

Scyphus. A podetium that widens at the top to form a cup.

Septum(a). An internal wall dividing cells or parts of cells.

Sessile. Fruiting body sitting on the thallus, not immersed.

Siliceous. Acid rocks; sand, flint, granite, etc, not calcareous.

Sinuate. Curved and recurved.

s.l., sensu lato. In a wide sense.

Soralium(a). Structure producing soredia. See p. XL.

Soredium. Small powdery propagule containing a few algal cells and fungal hyphae.

Spinules. Small, fine, short branchlets.

Spore (ascospore). A reproductive body of the fungus. For types See p. XVII.

Squamulose. Small leaf-like structures, lacking a lower cortex. See p. XIX.

Stellate. Star-shaped, radiating.

Striations. Small parallel ridges or lines.

Stroma. Compact sterile fungal tissue, often containing perithecia.

Substrate. Surface upon or in which the lichen grows.

Supralittoral zone. The area of the seashore above the tide line.

Terete. More or less circular in section, with a cortex all round.

Terricolous. Growing on soil, sand, peat, etc.

Tesselated. Like a tile floor.

Tetrachotomous. Divided into fours.

Thalline. Margin Found in lecanorine apothecia, containing both algal and fungal cells. See p. XXII.

Thallus. The body of the lichen containing both fungal and algal cells.

Thecium. The tissues comprising the paraphyses, asci and spores.

Tholus. The inner apical tissues of some asci.

Tomentose. Covered in fine hairs, like felt.

Trabeculum(a). Flattened "tendon-like" rhizinae.

Translucent. Allowing the light to pass through.

Tuberculate. Wart-like.

Tumid. Thick and swollen.

Uniseriate. In a single row.

Urceolate. Deeply concave, cup-shaped, with the margin incurved.

Var. Abbreviation for variety.

Verrucose. Warted.

TAXONOMIC INDEX

NOMENCLATURE

Since this book was first published, a new checklist of British Lichens has been issued (Hawksworth, James & Coppins, *Lichenologist* **12**:1-115, 1980; also available separately). Some names adopted in that list differ from those given here as a result of recent taxonomic studies. This index gives the current names (Roman type) for lichens included in this book (italic type), where these have changed. It also provides a cross-reference so those using the new checklist can locate species included, but under different names.

Anaptychia leucomelos = Heterodermia leucomelos
Anaptychia obscurata = Heterodermia obscurata
Anisomeridium biforme, see *Arthopyrenia biformis*
Arthonia didyma, see *A. lurida*
Arthonia didyma = A. vinosa
Arthonia lobata = A. phaeobaea
Arthonia lurida = A. didyma
Arthonia phaeobaea, see *A. lobata*
Arthonia vinosa, see *A. didyma*

PROPERTY OF PERSHORE COLLEGE OF HORTICULTURE LIBRARY

Arthopyrenia biformis = Anisomeridium biforme
Aspicilia lacustris = Hymenelia lacustris
Bacidia chlorococca = Scoliciosporum chlorococcum
Bacidia umbrina = Scoliciosporum umbrinum
Catapyrenium lachneum, see *Dermatocarpon hepaticum*
Catillaria griffithii = Cliostomum griffithii
Chrysothrix candelaris, see *Lepraria candelaris*
Chrysothrix chlorina, see *Lepraria chlorina*
Cladonia cervicornis subsp. verticillata, see *C. verticillata*
Cladonia verticillata = C. cervicornis subsp. verticillata
Cliostomum griffithii, see *Catillaria griffithii*
Coelocaulon aculeatum, see *Cornicularia aculeata*
Coelocaulon aculeatum subsp. hispidum, see *Cornicularia muricata*
Coelocaulon divergens, see *Cornicularia divergens*
Cornicularia aculeata = Coelocaulon aculeatum
Cornicularia divergens = Coelocaulon divergens
Cornicularia muricata = Coelocaulon aculeatum subsp. hispidum
Cystocoleus ebeneus, see *C. niger*
Cystocoleus niger = C. ebeneus
Dermatocarpon fluviatile = D. weberi
Dermatocarpon hepaticum = Catapyrenium lachneum
Dermatocarpon weberi, see D. fluviatile
Dimerella pineti = D. diluta
Diploschistes bryophilus = D. muscorum
Diploschistes muscorum, see *D. bryophilus*
Dirina repanda f. stenhammari, see *D. stenhammarii*
Dirina stenhammarii = D. repanda f. stenhammari
Heterodermia leucomelos, see *Anaptychia leucomelos*
Heterodermia obscurata, see *Anaptychia obscurata*
Huilia tuberculosa, see *Lecidea tumida*
Hymenelia lacustris, see *Lecanora lacustris*
Lecanactis lyncea, see *Opegrapha lyncea*
Lecanora albescens, see *L. dispersa* f. *albescens*
Lecanora chlarona = L. pulicaris
Lecanora dispersa f. *albescens* = L. albescens
Lecanora pulicaris, see *L. chlarona*
Lecidea lucida = Psilolechia lucida
Lecidea quernea = Pyrrhospora quernea
Lecidea tumida = Huilia tuberculosa
Lecidea wallrothii = Trapeliopsis wallrothii

Lepraria candelaris = Chrysothrix candelaris
Lepraria chlorina = Chrysothrix chlorina
Ochrolechia subviridis, see *O. yasudae*
Ochrolechia yasudae = O. subviridis
Omphalina hudsoniana, see *Coriscium viride*
Opegrapha conferta, see *O. confluens*
Opegrapha confluens = O. conferta
Opegrapha lyncea = Lecanactis lyncea
Parmelia afrorevoluta, see *P. revoluta*
Parmelia revoluta = P. afrorevoluta p.p.
Physconia pulverulacea, see *P. pulverulenta*
Physconia pulverulenta = P. pulverulacea
Polysporina simplex, see *Sarcogyne simplex*
Porina aenea, see *P. carpinea*
Porina carpinea = P. aenea
Protoblastenia cinnabarina = Lecidea cinnabarina
Psilolechia lucida, see *Lecidea lucida*
Pyrenula chlorospila, see *P. nitida*
Pyrenula nitida = P. chlorospila
Pyrrhospora quernea, see *Lecidea quernea*
Rhizocarpon concentricum, see *R. petraeum*
Rhizocarpon petraeum = R. concentricum
Rinodina gennarii, see *R. subexigua*
Rinodina subexigua = R. gennarii
Sarcogyne simplex = Polysporina simplex
Scoliciosporum chlorococcum, see *Bacidia chlorococca*
Scoliciosporum umbrinum, see *Bacidia umbrina*
Squamarina cartilaginea, see *S. crassa*
Squamarina crassa = S. cartilaginea
Stenocybe byssacea, see *S. pullatula*
Stenocybe pullatula = S. byssacea
Sticta dufourii = S. canariensis
Thamnolia vermicularis = T. vermicularis var. subuliformis
Trapelia involuta, see *T. ornata*
Trapelia ornata = T. involuta
Trapeliopsis wallrothii, see *Lecidea wallrothii*
Verrucaria baldensis, see *V. sphinctrina*
Verrucaria elaeomelaena = V. funckii
Verrucaria funckii, see *V. elaeomelaena*
Verrucaria halizoa, see *V. microspora*
Verrucaria microspora = V. halizoa
Verrucaria sphinctrina = V. baldensis